Ten Perfect Fingers

Published by:
Old Mountain Press, Inc.
2542 S. Edgewater Dr.
Fayetteville, NC 28303

www.oldmp.com

Cover Illustrated by Warren Hile
ISBN: 1-884778-64-X
Library of Congress Catalog Card Number: 99-61500

Ten Perfect Fingers.

First Edition
Manufactured in the United States of America
1 2 3 4 5 6 7 8 9 10

To Jarren with love...

CHAPTER I

L et me tell you, August in Los Angeles can be one miserable experience, especially in the inland valleys like in Arcadia where Mike and I live. Four to five months a year of intense heat sometimes coupled with a thick, nasty layer of smog — not exactly a choice time to be out and about in a car with no air conditioning, especially when you're five months pregnant. But out we were, and not even a sizzling hot Monday was going to spoil my mood today. Today was too big. Today was too exciting. Today was too overwhelming. The word "ultrasound" kept echoing in my mind. What a miracle of technology it is that they can image the features of an unborn baby using only sound waves. Just think, in less than one hour from now Mike and I will be getting our first glimpse of our son or daughter to be. The thought of it made me crazy.

I was like a kid waiting for my parents to wake up on Christmas morning. I had to shut the thought of it out of my mind. This was a mental thing, like driving cross-country and having to go to the bathroom. You just have to discipline yourself until you can find somewhere to stop. I kept thinking about those ultrasound photographs my friend Kelly once showed me of her son, Jameson, that were taken before he was born. Stop it, Brenda! Just focus on the trip. Just a few more miles and we'll be at the hospital.

I stared down at my swollen belly and cradled my arms around it. The smock I picked out for the occasion didn't even look like part of my clothing anymore. It was a cotton drop cloth covering some magnificent sculptural masterpiece about to be revealed to the world for the first time. The intense feelings of intimacy I felt earlier in the day with the baby started to well up again, and they reverberated throughout my body. I got those feelings a lot these days. Sometimes they were so intense I could feel the baby's eyes staring back at me when I looked down at my belly.

Everything was happening so fast now. Was I becoming detached in the process? Sometimes it was very hard for me to grasp that this pregnancy thing was real. Was it only a month ago that I was sticking my belly out everywhere I went just to prove to everyone within eyeshot that I really was pregnant? Now there's no room for any doubt. I walk in a room and my belly screams out "Hey, look at me. Is this woman pregnant or what?"

Mike had taken off work from the power company just for the occasion. It wasn't easy for him to get away, being a foreman and everything, especially on a Monday and especially to go make "baby pictures." But inside I could tell he knew it was going to be worth it. I had convinced him of that. This was going to shake all those detached overtones of indifference out of him and bring on some genuine excitement. This thing's gonna slap him in the face and say, "Hey, this is for real, buddy. That's your baby up on that screen! Lookie there...we have got ourselves a star!"

I had been waiting patiently for weeks for this day to arrive. I had asked my obstetrician, Dr. Suvannee, for an ultrasound when I first started to show.

"No," she said, "it's better that we wait a month or two so the baby can grow a little more. There will be more to see."

I started to think again about the ultrasound photo Kelly had shown me of her baby. You could see the outline of the baby's legs and arms and everything. I wondered if I would get to take home a print out like that.

At last we made the turn into the parking lot at Santa Teresita Hospital. The last time I was at Dr. Suvannee's office I was barely showing. I felt out of place sitting in her waiting room with all these women who looked like they were ready to give birth right next to the magazine rack. This time I was the fattest, most voluptuously pregnant woman in the room, or at least it felt that way. We proudly strutted up to the receptionist's window to announce our arrival.

"Hello, Brenda. You look great!" said one of Dr. Suvannee's receptionists.

wasn't coming with me. He nodded at me to go on without him, and to reassure me he gave his usual "be a brave girl" wink. The sister led me into a small examining room.

"Please, sister, I want my husband to come with me," I pleaded with her. "He took off work just to be here. It's really important he sees this. You see, he doesn't believe I'm pregnant."

The nun didn't reply but continued to prepare the examining room, pulling the drapes closed, unwinding cables, and switching on the equipment. I felt a surge of panic and started to babble at her. "Please, I need him here. Why can't he come in? It's his baby too. Why are you doing this to us? I want him to see."

"We want to see first, Mrs. Winner," she answered. "Mr. Winner can come in later. Now please lie here, and lift your top for me."

She smeared conducting jelly over my belly and placed the ice-cold metallic probe on my skin without warming it in her hands first. She turned around and switched on the monitor console. The screen filled with static. Jagged lines criss-crossed across the monitor until suddenly the picture snapped into a steady gray haze. A vague image resembling a wisp of white smoke appeared on the monitor.

"What's that?" I asked.

The nun didn't answer. Instead she continued on with her examination, unperturbed by my protests.

"What is it, dammit?" I cried out. She glanced back in my direction, but then returned her attention to the monitor screen. Feeling frustrated, I sat up. The ultrasound sensor slipped out of her hand and banged loudly onto the tabletop.

"I want Mike, and I want him in here now!" I yelled at her. Finally she looked me in the eyes, and I started to burst into tears. "I'm not going to do this until Michael is in here!" I sobbed. I pulled down my smock and struggled to get off the examining table.

The sister finally gave in to my demands and silently left the room. Shaking and shivering, I sat back up on the table, wiping away the tears with the back of my hand and smearing my makeup in the process. Why was this moment being stolen from us? I looked up at the monitor, somehow expecting to still be able to see something. I gently patted my belly.

"Are you still there?" I asked it. I felt a slight stirring sensation that reassured me. Suddenly Mike appeared at the door, and I flung myself into his arms and started sobbing again.

"It's OK, baby. I'm here now," he said to me in a soothing voice while stroking my hair. "It's OK. Here, blow your nose."

The sister returned, this time bringing with her a kind-looking gentleman wearing a white coat. He mentioned his name, but I couldn't remember it because of my sobbing. He appeared to be the head radiologist. He took the sensor between his palms to warm it before placing it on my belly. His presence seemed to calm me, and he began to move the sensor very gently over my belly. He watched the screen intently. The wisp of smoke appeared again.

"So, is everything all right, Mrs. Winner?" the doctor said in a soft voice. He spoke so kindly. His words left me feeling much more warm and comfortable.

"Uh-huh. I just wanted Mike to be in the room," I replied. I looked over toward Mike, but his eyes were fixed on the screen, mesmerized by the image on the monitor. The doctor also fixed his eyes on the screen, and he didn't look away as he continued to probe and question me.

"Why did you request this ultrasound, Mrs. Winner?" he asked me.

"I wanted to know how far along I was, doctor."

"I see," he paused. "Any problems with your pregnancy?"

"Oh no, none at all," I replied. "It's been wonderful. Ask Dr. Suvannee."

"And how do you feel?"

"Never better!" I answered. Suddenly an unusual image appeared on the screen. "Wow! What's that?"

"That's a leg, Mrs. Winner."

A leg? That's my baby's leg! I could see it. Now the wisp of smoke looked just like my baby's leg!

"Can you see his foot?" I asked.

The doctor momentarily turned his head away from the monitor. "Do you know that it's a boy, then?" he asked.

"No, I don't. We're hoping for a boy. We think it's a boy. But I don't want to know, so don't tell me. OK?"

The doctor turned his attention back to the monitor. "OK, there are the feet and toes. Can you see?"

My heart pounded with excitement. Mike's eyes were still fixed on the screen but were filling with tears. Everything was becoming more distinguishable, and we watched in awe as the doctor pointed out the baby's heart, beating strongly and full of life, pumping away right before our eyes.

"My God, Mike, look!" I shouted.

A miniature hand floated out toward us from the screen with five fingers splayed open. Then the other hand became visible, also with its fingers spread wide. One of the hands closed and opened rhythmically, as if it was trying to reach out and grab hold of the monitor screen.

"He's waving at us!" I cried out. Mike squeezed on my hand, but he wasn't able to speak. Tears started to pour down my cheeks as I waved back. "Look Mike...ten perfect fingers. Count them. Our baby is perfect!"

I was ready to spend the rest of the day just watching those incredible fingers, but the radiologist pulled the sensor from my belly and told the nun to shut down the machine. He said goodbye and then left the room so I could get dressed.

"When do I get the pictures?" I asked the sister brightly. After seeing those fingers I was ready to sit down to tea with the Wicked Witch of the West.

"We don't give them out anymore," she answered without looking up.

"Oh yes you do!" I contested indignantly. "My girlfriend was here just last month, and you gave her one."

"We'll give it to you in the office."

Disgusted, I gave up haggling with the nun and started for the door. The sister walked with me, and as I was about to leave the room she whispered "God be with you" into my ear. Then she kissed me on the cheek. I noticed that she had tears in her eyes.

"Well thanks," I answered with a bit of confusion. I wasn't about to quiz this woman about what was bothering her. I just wanted to get some distance between her and me as soon as possible. As we headed back to the reception area, I felt like I was walking on a cushion of air. I pretended not to notice that the sister's eyes were still trained on me.

I grabbed Mike in my arms. "You're a daddy!" I laughed.

"Sure am!" he smiled, obviously still excited about what had happened.

"Hey," I said, turning toward the girls behind the receptionist's desk, "we're the proud parents of ten perfect fingers. Congratulate us!"

"Sure," said Sylvia quietly. Grace didn't turn around. "Dr. Suvannee will call you."

"Great!" I said. She's probably going to call us about the photo, I thought to myself.

On the way back to the house, I couldn't stop talking about those little hands we had seen back in the hospital. Mike wasn't saying much, but the irrepressible grin on his face said everything I needed to know.

We had been home about two hours when Dr. Suvannee finally phoned. She asked me if Mike was still home, and could we both come down to her office right away. She said she had something very important to talk to us about and needed to see us immediately.

CHAPTER II

W hen we got back to the doctor's office, I could tell by the look on the receptionist's face that something was definitely wrong.

"Why so glum girls?" I asked. "Having a bad day?"

Dr. Suvannee immediately appeared in the doorway and led us into her office. Very good service, I thought, considering the office was full of people waiting for appointments. She must feel guilty about missing the ultrasound session. Oh well, handing us an ultrasound photo would only take a minute anyway.

"Have you seen the results, Dr. Suvannee?" I asked her enthusiastically. "When can we get the pictures?"

"Brenda, Mike, please sit down." Dr. Suvannee's voice was unusually stern and serious. "I don't know how to say this so I'll just say it. The ultrasound results were not good. Your baby is incompatible with life."

When people first hear bad news you can expect to see many different immediate reactions. There are the hysterical types, prone to dramatics and boisterous fits of breast-beating denial. "You're lying to me, doctor, I know you're lying!" Sound familiar? Then there are the Kleenex Busters, who sob uncontrollably whether there is any good reason to cry or not. And then there are the rest of us, the ones who bad news just sort of bounces off of, like the words never even registered in their heads. Is the world coming to an end tomorrow night? Hey, I think I'll pack a tuna sandwich for lunch. The two statements have an equivalent effect on me.

Somewhere underneath I knew that I should be stunned, shocked, maybe even a bit giddy, but on the surface I was calmed by a strange confidence. I felt like someone who just walked away unscathed from a really bad traffic accident. Dr. Suvannee's words began to fade from my ears. I couldn't even follow what she was saying anymore. It was like she was speaking to me in some foreign language. I kept waiting to be hit by an avalanche of emotion. It never seemed to materialize.

"What does incompatible with life mean?" I asked rather dim-wittedly.

"Your baby will not survive outside the womb."

Not survive out of the womb, I thought. Does that mean I have to carry this baby forever? I turned over toward Mike and saw he had jumped ship over to the Kleenex Busters. He was sobbing so hard that his entire body was shaking. Wild thoughts started to drift through my mind. I saw myself in high school, now carrying a full-grown teenager inside me and having to carry his books around from class to class. I had a terrifying vision of myself, frail and gray and knitting in a rocking chair, but still pregnant.

"How long do I have to carry him?" I heard myself ask.

"Brenda, your baby has anencephaly and won't live more than a few hours or days after it is born. I'm so sorry."

Mike flung his arms around me. He was still sobbing, and his tears were running down my neck. Why was he crying so hard? I'm trying to talk to the doctor, sweetheart.

"What about the heart?" I asked her. "If the baby is dying, why is the heart beating so strongly?"

"Anencephaly means 'without a brain.' The baby has no brain, Brenda. It never developed one and can't survive without one."

"Oh yeah?" I interjected skeptically. "Then what is making it kick so hard?"

"The baby has strong organs, and so long as it is on mother's life support, it will grow quite normally like any other fetus. But once the baby is born its own brain has to take over that life support. Without a brain, death is inevitable."

It struck me as rather strange that I hadn't joined in the sobbing festivities with Mike by now. But I couldn't even feel the hint of a tear coming on. As hard as I was trying to force myself, I just couldn't believe that my baby was going to die. Just that instant I felt the baby kick again. It promoted the strong feelings of detachment I was getting, as if I wasn't even a player in the story

14

anymore. I felt like I was watching the situation as an outside observer. That poor woman over there...her baby is going to die.

But then another set of thoughts flushed through me. What if Dr. Suvannee was mistaken? After all, she wasn't even present for the ultrasound examination.

There had been no mistake, Dr. Suvannee assured me. The precise age of the fetus is determined from the diameter of the cranium, she explained. The sister and the doctor had both searched for the skull, but the baby simply didn't have one. Finally, they determined the baby's age from the length of its femur.

Dr. Suvannee sighed, shaking her head in frustration. "I still can't believe it myself. You had such a perfect pregnancy."

She looked at me with a puzzled look, surprised by the calm reaction I was having toward this whole thing. She no doubt wondered if I properly grasped the full meaning of what she just told me. The answer, of course, was that I did not. She clasped my hand in hers, and I noticed her eyes were tearing. She reached over to one of the bookshelves lining her office walls and pulled down a very impressive looking oversized volume. It was bound in red leather and imprinted with gold lettering.

"Let me show you what the condition looks like," she said in a gentle voice.

She handed me the book that was now opened to a page containing a photograph of a grotesquely deformed baby. Underneath the photo was the caption "anencephalic monster."

"No," I replied coolly, "that's not *my* baby. My baby is strong, beautiful. He's not a monster!" Who could show such a horrible picture to an expectant mother like that?

"You're right. Of course your baby doesn't look like that. I'm sorry. Perhaps I shouldn't have shown this to you. I simply wanted you to see how the condition manifests itself. Indeed, anencephalic infants very often look like perfectly formed babies except that, as you can see, the top of their skull and their brain are absent. I delivered an anencephalic baby seven years ago, and it looked completely normal in every other way."

"You delivered one seven years ago?" I asked with some surprise.

Dr. Suvannee nodded.

"What causes it? Was it something I did?"

15

"No, Brenda. You didn't do this. No one knows what causes it."

"Could it have been the pill?" I asked.

"No."

"I stopped smoking!"

"No."

"I stopped drinking!"

"No, Brenda. Don't do this to yourself."

"How come they don't know what causes it?"

"There simply hasn't been enough research done. The condition is very rare. Only one in every thousand babies is anencephalic. Believe me...."

"So what are our options?" Mike interrupted, having pulled himself together somewhat. The pain in his eyes was almost too much for me to bear.

Dr. Suvannee straightened in her chair. "In this respect you are more fortunate than my other patient," she said. "She had a perfectly normal pregnancy just like Brenda's. Strong fetal heartbeat, no abnormal signs. We didn't find out the baby's condition until after it was born. It was a terrible shock for the parents and just as terrible of a shock for me. At least you have time on your side to come to terms with your tragedy."

Mike and I exchanged glances and then returned our attention to the doctor as she continued.

"You have two options. You can choose to abort, or you can carry to term and possibly donate the baby's organs for a transplant. Anencephaly is one of the very few medical conditions where abortion is permitted right into the third trimester of pregnancy."

"What happens if Brenda carries to term?" asked Mike.

"Sixty percent of these babies are stillborn because the natural trauma of birth is magnified enormously for them due to the absence of a protective skull. If the baby does survive, it will live only a few days, perhaps even a few weeks, but certainly no longer. During that time it will be given what is called 'comfort care.' It will be kept warm and will be given food, if it will take it."

"That's it?" Mike asked, his voice thinly masking his frustration.

"I'm afraid so, Mike," Dr. Suvannee answered. "There is nothing more that medical science can do for these babies."

"But what about Brenda?" Mike asked. "What will happen to her? Will she be all right?"

"Physically speaking, there is no reason Brenda shouldn't come out of this just fine. Being so far along, she will be laid up for a good four to six weeks if you choose to abort. And there is always a slight risk with a second or third trimester abortion that the mother may not be able to conceive again, but that risk is really quite minimal. My personal advice would be to think about having another baby as soon as you can, and put this one behind you."

"But...will the next one ...," Mike stuttered. The words were too terrible for him to finish.

"Be anencephalic too?" Dr. Suvannee answered, completing Mike's sentence. "The chances are extremely slim, Mike. A mother having two anencephalic babies is very rare. There's no reason you and Brenda can't have a healthy, perfectly formed baby next time. In the meantime, I suggest you take this one step at a time." She took Mike's hand in her own and patted it reassuringly. "Go home. Think about your options. Whatever you decide, I'll support you 100 percent. It's going to be a tough ride emotionally for both of you. Take the time to come to terms with your loss. The hospital has an excellent grief counseling program...."

CHAPTER III

The drive home from Santa Teresita Hospital was only a few miles, but the road seemed to stretch on forever and ever. A deafening silence had consumed me. Mike was deep in a quiet trance of his own. Inside my head, though, the thoughts were bouncing around like little ping pong balls. It all started to make sense now...the cold shoulder during the ultrasound...the run-around about getting a photograph of the results...the tears in the nun's eyes. She was only trying to prevent me from noticing that the baby's head was missing.

I remembered the day Dr. Suvannee offered to perform an AFP test for me. AFP stands for "alpha fetal protein," a blood test that can detect birth defects such as spina bifida and anencephaly early on during pregnancy. Although the test must be offered to all pregnant women by law, it is accurate only when administered between the fifteenth and nineteenth weeks of pregnancy. Of course I refused, thinking that I had nothing to worry about.

And for all I knew I was right not to worry. I had none of the typical pregnancy problems. There was no morning sickness, no swelling. Even my rate of weight gain was perfect. I almost felt guilty that things were going so smoothly. How naive! I guess I just believed that if something was wrong with the baby, I would automatically miscarry.

I felt the baby shift position inside me. As usual, I laid a comforting hand gently down on my belly.

"You're as good as dead as far as everyone else is concerned," I whispered down to my belly, "but not to me. Why? Why don't I want to get rid of you?"

I looked at Mike and wondered what he thought of me. Did he think that I was responsible for what happened? Did I let him down? I couldn't see any anger in his face. This was a man who was no stranger to misfortune, having lost his younger brother to a freak accident a few years earlier. This can't be any easier for him now. I have to be strong for him. This thing is not going to tear us apart from one another.

Mike must have sensed that I was preoccupied with self-doubt. He took my hand to comfort me.

"Are you all right?" he asked me.

"I am, honestly," I replied.

I hardly believed my own words. So far I was keeping a good grip on things, but I kept waiting for that giant tidal wave of emotion to hit shore. I'm probably just in shock. Any moment now the facade is going to crumble, and I am just going to totally lose it.

"Stop the car!" I yelled suddenly as we passed by the local supermarket. "I have to tell Donna."

Mike gaped at me with a puzzled look on his face.

"You know, Donna, the checker at the supermarket. She sold us the home pregnancy kit."

"Yeah, but do you really have to tell her? And right now?"

"I'll be right back!" I answered.

Mike pulled into the supermarket parking lot, and I hopped out. I suppose Mike must have thought I was crazy, but somehow I felt very bonded with Donna. She had been there with me all the way from my first days of pregnancy and was very supportive. Right now I needed all the support I could get. Donna spotted me immediately as I walked in the front door.

"So, how did the ultrasound go?" she asked, bypassing the small talk.

"Do you have a minute?" I answered. Suddenly I felt a hot flash. How was I going to break the news to her? I almost panicked and made a run for it, but instead I just blurted out the bad news.

"The baby isn't going to live."

Donna didn't hesitate. She instantly burst into tears. Oh my God, I thought to myself. Why did I do this? Why did I come in here? Was it just to make this poor woman cry? I wished like anything I could take it all back and tell her "Hey, it's OK. I was kidding.... Nothing's really wrong."

"Everything's OK," I soothed her, interchanging roles with my sympathizer for a minute. "Mike and I are OK. The baby is anencephalic, and as soon as I find out what the hell that means, I'll let you know."

On the way home I turned to Mike and said, "We have to research this thing."

"Research?" Mike answered. "Brenda, you need to rest. You've had a terrible shock. You need to take it easy."

"Take it easy?" How could he say that? Our baby was gone, snatched away from us by some horrible genetic miscue that I never even heard of before. And here I was, not even having the slightest clue as to what the hell this thing was really all about. No, I could not take it easy, not this time. I was going to get to the bottom of this one.

"I'm fine," I snapped at Mike. "You take it easy!"

Our dog, Porky, was waiting for us as we walked in the front door, his tail sweeping back and forth across the matted carpet. I bent down to greet him. I felt Mike's hand on my shoulder, and I turned around and fell into his arms, embracing him tightly.

"Are you all right?" he asked me in a gentle whisper.

"I'm fine. Really I am," I answered. "Please don't hate me for it, but I don't feel bad. I don't know what's wrong with me."

We sat down together on the couch, and our eyes wandered to the telephone. Who do you call first with this kind of bad news? Suddenly the phone rang. Someone else made that decision for us.

The caller was a friend of ours named Bobbye. She called to see how the ultrasound had gone.

"I can't talk right now," I said to her, "our baby doesn't have a brain!" Then I hung up on her without any further hoopla or explanation.

Mike gave me a horrified look as if to say with his expression "What are you, nuts?", but before he could say anything the phone rang again. This time it was Karen — another friend of the family. I just laid the news out for her plain and simple, although in a somewhat less abrupt fashion than the way I broke the news to Bobbye. Mike continued to gape at me, his mouth hanging wide open with disbelief. I only answered him with a shrug, as if to say "Well, what am I supposed to say?"

"You two hold on right there," said Karen. "I'm coming over."

"Great!" I answered.

"Should I bring," Karen hesitated, "the baby?"

"Well of course," I said. What did she think I was going to do — go psycho and kidnap her baby? "Of course you should bring Jessica with you."

Karen stayed for about an hour. She sat and comforted Mike while I played with Jessica, her adorable three-month-old daughter. I was tickling her, and in the midst of our playfulness I teased "I guess I'm just not going to have one like you!" Mike and Karen stared at me like I was some patient on the critical list in the intensive care ward. Although they were sitting only a short distance away, they were discussing me as if I wasn't even in the same room.

"I'm so worried about Brenda," I heard Mike say to Karen. A few stray tears were still rolling down his cheeks. "Just look at her. It hasn't hit her yet. What am I going to do when it hits her?"

I kept playing with the baby, content to remain detached from the conversation. Karen asked Mike endless questions about what exactly was the problem and what causes it, and every time Mike could only just sit there and answer the same thing: "We don't know...." When Karen left, I cornered Mike in the kitchen.

"What did I tell you?" I said. "We need more facts before we start telling everybody about the ultrasound."

"If we don't call them, they're going to call us," he answered.

"OK then, you call them," I said. I was taking the cowardly way out by making Mike break the bad news to everybody, but I couldn't face all those questions. Not until I had a few more answers.

Mike picked up the phone, and I realized the first person he was going to call was his father — not the best choice for a sympathetic or sensitive ear to pour your soul out to in a crisis.

"What the hell does she want to carry that thing for?" I heard him bark at Mike over the telephone. "Tell her to get rid of it."

Dad was not the type to mince words.

"Don't worry about what Dad said," Mike reassured me after he hung up. "It doesn't matter, honey."

Mike's mom was the next one to get the bad news.

"We just got back from having the ultrasound, and the baby is anencephalic. It doesn't have a brain. No, I don't know what that means.... I don't know.... I don't know ," he kept repeating. "It's fatal.... No, it's definitely fatal.... Yeah, she's OK."

Now came the time to call my parents. I made Mike break the news to my mother. Finally I took the phone from him and found Mom to be very calm and collected. She didn't seem to be shaken up at all, or at least not the way I expected her to be.

"Are you all right, honey?" she asked tenderly.

"I'm fine, Mom," I answered.

"I'm so glad you're not aborting, sweetheart. You have to believe in miracles. You know, God could just zap that little baby for you. He might just touch your baby and give him a brain."

"Right, Mom," I replied, humoring her, "he sure might." I resisted the urge to comment on her spiritual pronouncements.

My stepfather came onto the phone and added, "We love you. Remember that. Whatever you decide to do, we're behind you. If you need anything," he continued, "just call us."

I appreciated that extra note of support. Sometimes my mother's religious zeal was too much for me to take. Mom was from the old school. She was the type that went to church every Sunday her entire life, at least until she decided to leave my dad. The Church excommunicated her for divorcing him, and she took the whole thing very personally. She wanted to remarry, but of course a Catholic wedding was out of the question.

My impression was that Mom still felt a lot of anger over the whole ordeal of the divorce and the way she was treated by the Church because of it. Nonetheless she still held on tenaciously to her own version of faith, even without the Pope's official blessing. She still blessed the house with holy water, but also talked a lot about "karma" and a lot of other ideas that weren't exactly in line with standard Church dogma. She also believed that what goes around comes around, and although she had her problems with the Church, she was careful to never cut herself off from its teachings entirely.

"You call everyone else," I told Mike after I hung up the phone. "After talking to your dad and my mom, I've had enough enlightenment for one day!"

The next day I headed out for the Arcadia Public Library. It certainly was not a place where I spent much time before. As I walked in, I spotted a pleasant-looking librarian sitting at the front desk. She seemed friendly enough, but I immediately froze as I tried to think of what to say to her. What topic should I ask for? If I ask for "causes of birth defects" the librarian might think I'm some degenerate mother trying to find a way to deform my unborn baby.

"Where can I look up some medical terms, please?" I finally asked her.

"Medical section. Downstairs on the left, behind the reference section."

I made my way down to the medical section with no problem and started to scan the shelves, still wondering just what it was I was looking for. On the second shelf I recognized a copy of the same book that Dr. Suvannee had shown me in her office. I pulled the volume from the shelf and opened it to the page that had the photo of the "anencephalic monster." I began reading the passage underneath the photo.

"The abnormality involves the derivatives of the most anterior portion of the neural tube and the structures that encase it. The cranial vault is invariably absent and the cerebral hemispheres are completely missing or reduced to small masses attached to the base of the skull. Frontal bones are not present above the supraorbital ridge, and parietal bones either are entirely absent or consist only of a narrow ridge. The anterior cranial fossae...."

The text went on and on. This was too much information, but at the same time it was not enough. I pulled volume after volume from the shelf, looking up "anencephaly" and "neural tube defects" in the index of each one. I kept finding the same words over and over: "complete absence of a brain," and "underdeveloped neocortex," and "the condition is 100 percent fatal." Still none of these books were telling me what I really wanted to know. What causes anencephaly? Has an anencephalic baby ever been used as a donor in a transplant? Is there any risk to carrying an anencephalic fetus to full term? I stared down the long aisle of books and realized that I was never going to find the answer to my most important question of all, at least not here in the library. That question was why was all this happening? What possible purpose could there be to all this? I decided that I needed to talk again to Dr. Suvannee. Maybe she could hit me with a few fresh answers.

Although I had made a point of stopping at the grocery store the previous day to break the bad news to Donna, in the emotional chaos of the moment I had neglected to buy any food. Poor Mike was sent off to work with a packet of stale saltine crackers and a peach that was way past its prime. Now seemed a good time to walk to the store, pick up a few things, and mull over the findings of my visit to the library.

As I waddled the final steps to the front door, a stranger ran up and very chivalrously held it open for me. I thanked him graciously and pulled a shopping cart from the rack. Behind me was a young mother single-handedly negotiating a pair of twin toddlers and their stroller through the glass doors. One shoulder was straddled with a huge diaper bag, and she had a bulky purse strapped over her other shoulder. I opened the door for her and smiled with an apologetic grin.

"When you're pregnant, they treat you with so much respect and consideration," she said as she separated a shopping cart from the stack for herself. "It's that Mother Earth fertility goddess thing, you know?" She groaned a little as she lifted her second twin into the grocery cart. "But as soon as you have the kid, forget it!"

She folded up her stroller and gave me a cagey smile. "Remember these times, my dear," she warned. "The pregnancy is the best part of the whole thing, and it's over far too quickly."

I nodded and agreed.

"So how far along are you anyway?" she asked, staring down at my swollen belly.

"Almost six months," I answered, "but the baby's not going to live."

"Oh, I'm so sorry."

"Please, don't be. Let me explain it to you."

I leaned back against a pallet rack stacked full with diet soda and proceeded to tell this woman — a total stranger — my story. She was the perfect audience. No detail was too small or trivial. Her twins began to fuss, but she never broke eye contact with me for a moment. I wondered why I felt so compelled to tell this woman my deepest, most personal inner feelings. Was it all really that important, what was happening to me, or was I blowing this thing way out of proportion to satisfy some sick delusion I was forming in my head?

"We've decided to carry to term and donate the organs," I heard myself say to her. I felt strange saying it to her, though, because I suddenly realized that Mike and I hadn't even discussed the options yet.

"I have a little boy at home who's desperately sick," the woman answered. "He's got biliary atresia, and a liver transplant is our only hope. Without it he will die within a few months. But we're at the bottom of the waiting list." She began to cry. "Organs are so...scarce."

I felt the baby kick inside me, and then suddenly it came to me. It was the answer to that all-important question that haunted me ever since I first heard the bad news. My baby can save her baby. That's it! That is why this baby is being born. We have a chance to save another baby's life!

CHAPTER IV

It wasn't long after I arrived home from the grocery store that I made another call to Dr. Suvannee. She said she had spoken with Loma Linda Hospital about donating our baby's organs. She told me that only the heart valves and the cornea of the eye could be used legally. I was shocked. Why only the heart valves and cornea? Why not the liver and the rest of the organs? She said they had refused the other organs, and she mentioned something about the brain death law. She seemed confused, and she said she would inquire more about the procedures. For now, she insisted, I was to concentrate on taking it easy and to get lots of rest.

How frustrating! My conversation with Dr. Suvannee just complicated things. I wasn't getting any answers, and I was definitely starting to get desperate. When was I going to get a straight answer from somebody? Most of all, I didn't understand what brain death had to do with anything. First they tell me the reason my baby is going to die is because it has no brain, and now they tell me I can't donate its organs because its brain isn't dead yet. How is that supposed to make any sense?

I couldn't get it out of my mind that my chance meeting with the woman in the grocery store was somehow guided by fate. I finally found that something special that I could do for my baby — help another baby survive. I kept wondering how my baby felt about the whole situation. "Don't give up!" I could picture the baby saying, as if every time I felt a little kick I was being prodded into digging a little deeper. It was uncanny how every time I

26

thought of something new to do, or got hold of some new information or lead, the baby would stir. I took it as a sign that I had to continue my quest. After all, if the baby didn't want me to move on this thing, why did it keep encouraging me like that?

Later that evening, after we went to bed, I spent a long and restless night, lying sleeplessly in my pajamas. I churned the events of the day over and over again in my mind. It seemed like daylight was never going to come, that I was never going to get the chance to go out there and find some more answers.

The next morning my friend Bobbye came by with her four-year-old daughter, Amanda. I had been baby-sitting Amanda quite a bit during the past few months, but Bobbye seemed a little reluctant to leave her with me.

"Are you sure she won't be a bother today?" she asked me.

"Yes! Honestly, I would feel worse if she wasn't here," I answered.

Amanda was old enough to be fully aware of my pregnancy, although all the talk she had overheard about babies dying and transplants had her both a little worried and little curious. She was a sweet little girl and was very smart. She very quickly adapted to my new agenda, playing by herself while I hustled for information on the phone. She was so patient, asking me if "I was done with business and could play now" every day right before lunchtime. We were quickly settling into a new routine.

Later one night our friends Smily and Christi stopped in and spent the night while on their way to Phoenix. We stayed up most of the night talking about what had happened and the best way to deal with the situation. At one point the issue of insurance came up. Both Mike and Smily had the same health insurance carrier, since they both worked for the same union.

Early the next morning I called our insurance carrier, Lineco. They told me that they would cover me at Santa Teresita, but that they would cover me at another hospital only if it was necessary to save the baby's life. Since the baby was not going to live, any other procedure, such as an organ donation, would not be covered.

Now I was really starting to get bummed. I talked it over with Christi that night. She agreed that, since Santa Teresita was a Catholic hospital, there was little chance they would agree to an organ donation. Then I thought of Loma Linda Hospital. If anyone can do this kind of thing, and do it right, it's Loma Linda. For Christ's sake they transplanted a baboon heart into a human baby a few years back, didn't they? What I want to do is a cakewalk compared to transplanting animal parts into live human babies. Then suddenly Christi came up with a brilliant twist. Why not call them up, offer the organs for transplant, call it even, and then I'll just walk away — a kind of even trade, if you will. It sounded like a great idea. I could give them my family history or whatever they needed to match my baby up with a suitable transplant candidate.

The next morning I put Christi's brilliant plan into action. I called Loma Linda and asked for the head of OB/GYN. Some doctor came onto the line, and he introduced himself as Dr. Brothers. I immediately laid my best guaranteed, no-way-you-can-turn-me-down, super-dooper sales spiel on him.

"Hello, my name is Brenda Winner. I'm five and half months pregnant with an anencephalic fetus. The father and I have decided to carry the baby to term and donate the organs. Since my insurance won't cover the costs to donate, how about if I donate the baby's organs, and we call it even? You know, I'll deliver the baby, you transplant the organs, and I'll walk away. Would that be possible?"

As I anxiously awaited what I was sure would be his grateful reply, I suddenly thought of the mountain of paperwork I might now be in for.

"I am sorry about your situation," the doctor replied, "and I know this must be a trying time for you. It is also very tragic. But what you are asking is against the law, and there isn't a doctor anywhere that would attempt to use the organs before brain death occurs."

The doctor then went on and began to tell me the criteria for brain death.

"Wait a minute," I interrupted, "those criteria don't apply to this case, where the brain is absent, right?"

Dr. Brothers explained that the Right-To-Life groups would call such a procedure fetal abuse to use these babies solely for organ donation. We would be trampling on the baby's right to die with dignity. The only thing that they could do is give the baby comfort care, no matter how badly the organs were needed.

I interrupted him again. But what if we were to wait for brain death to occur? Could we donate then?

No, he answered. By the time brain death occurs, it is too late. The organs have degenerated to the point where a viable transplant is no longer possible.

"This is such a tragedy, Mrs. Winner," he consoled me. "The best thing you can do is put this behind you. You can probably have other children. My advice is to put this thing behind you because there is nothing that you or anyone else can do."

"Oh yeah, bet me mister!" I yelled into the mouthpiece after he hung up the phone. I was astonished by what I had just heard. How could he say that to me, "put it all behind you"? How can I put this all behind me when I know there's a baby out there that might be saved if I can just find someone with the guts to take me up on this thing?

I sat and thought for a moment and wondered if I really was trampling on the dignity of the anencephalic infants of the world. People are acting like I should be ashamed of what I'm trying to do. Dr. Brothers didn't even want to discuss it with me. What is so dignified about some morbid death vigil where you just keep this poor brainless baby warm and pretend like it's not going to die? I don't get it. I guess if you call it "comfort care" that makes it dignified. I wonder if they also call what they're doing for babies who die waiting for transplants "comfort care." It sounds to me like they're doing the exact same thing in both situations — absolutely nothing at all.

Then I began to think about the other parents of anencephalics. Do they think that taking their child's organs to in order save another baby's life is undignified? Am I really all alone on this? How many of them would think that there is something shameful and humiliating about what we're trying to do? Or do you have to be a so-called "expert" to see the indignity of it all? We're talking about saving hundreds of lives here!

This whole argument of "trampled dignity" sounded ridiculous to me. Are we parents going to bow our heads in humiliation because we saved someone else's baby? Why can't they let the parents decide for themselves whether or not to donate their baby's organs for transplantation? After all, isn't it their dignity that's at stake here? What about the dignity of the babies who die waiting for transplants? What is dignified about two babies dying when one might live?

I knew there had to be a doctor or a hospital somewhere that would go along with me. After all, this was all such nonsense. Dr. Brothers was in such a hurry to change the subject on me, especially when I mentioned the words "organ donation." End of phone call. What is keeping this thing such a big secret?

Maybe this is just a California thing. I once lived in Tucson, and I remembered that they had a good heart transplant center there. Maybe they will help us. I mapped out my strategy and dialed long distance information for the number of the University of Arizona Medical Center.

I asked the front desk for the OB/GYN department. A man's voice answered. I ran down my speech for him. "Hello, my name is ...," etc., etc. The man at the other end listened very patiently, but basically gave me the same answers as I got from Loma Linda.

"I'm terribly sorry. This is such a tragedy. You are right, the organs are needed, but...." I could predict almost word-for-word what he was going to say next.

I interrupted, asking if the law was different in Arizona. He informed me that it was an international law. In order to protect the dying and their right to die with dignity, a person is not determined to be dead until brain function has ceased totally. This is especially the case when organ donation is involved.

I interrupted again, asking if he knew any statistics on how many babies there were waiting for organ transplants. He replied that about five hundred babies a year die waiting for heart, liver, or kidney transplants in the U.S., mainly because organs are so scarce. But he added that nothing could be done before brain death is determined, even in a life-or-death situation.

I asked him if he thought I was some kind of sicko for wanting to donate my baby's organs immediately after birth. He said no, but that was the issue in which the controversy lies. To take the heart or any other organ would be to initiate the cause of death.

Since they won't take the organs for transplantation, I asked next, what would they do instead? How does the baby actually die?

"Although the brain stem is often intact at birth and is able to control the heart and muscles, it quickly deteriorates since it lacks the intelligence to breathe or swallow properly. The usual cause of death is either starvation or asphyxia. We give the babies comfort care, which basically means keeping them warm, since there is nothing else that can be done for these unfortunate babies."

With that our conversation ended. He wished me luck and thanked me for my generosity and said goodbye. I realized that I did not even ask him for his name. But he used that new favorite expression of mine, "comfort care." Sounds to me that if these babies could feel anything, they would be in agony. Could you imagine the headache that having no skull could bring on? For their entire lives the babies just lie there in misery and wait to die. And they call it comfort care.

A sharp chill ran up and down my spine. What if the babies really could feel pain? What if the first and last thing my baby will ever know is horrible pain and anguish? The thought of it terrified me. Yet somehow the thought of an abortion at this point in my pregnancy sounded worse. Organ donation sounded like the best compromise. My baby doesn't suffer by slowly choking to death, and someone else's life can be saved at the same time.

I looked down at my belly and started talking to it. I explained that I really was a nice person. This organ donation idea was simply the best thing I could come up with under the circumstances.

"At least he sounded more positive than that Brothers guy," I grumbled to my bulging abdomen. I was acting like my entire phone conversation had been forwarded straight down the umbilical cord, loud and clear, on a special conference call line. I listened, almost expecting to hear "Yeah, right on!" for an answer.

I caught a glimpse of little Amanda peeking out from behind the doorway. For a four-year-old, catching someone talking to their belly is not so much an embarrassment as something to giggle at, and Amanda seemed quite amused. I tried to change the subject by asking her what she was doing, but she was too sharp for that.

"I'm just wondering if the baby is going to answer you," Amanda replied.

Amanda had caught me doing things like this too often to be fooled. So I just shrugged and told her, "Not yet, sweetheart!"

I needed someone else to talk to, but whom? I began a massive phone calling campaign. Any hospital I could think of, any doctor I could think of, I called them all. I regularly combed the phone books at the library for new numbers. But I always got the same old story — lots of sympathy, but no substance. I even tried calling hospitals in Japan and Europe, but still with no results. I was succeeding in running up our phone bill, but I still was not finding the right person to talk to. I needed someone with knowledge and experience specifically with anencephalics. Suddenly I overheard someone on the television mention Children's Hospital. On an impulse I opened the phone book, picked up the phone, and dialed the number for Children's Hospital. I asked for the Chief Obstetrician.

A gentleman by the name of Dr. Lynn Murphree came on the phone and asked how he could help me. I gave him my usual speech, and in turn I got the same old speech back about "putting this thing behind you" and comfort care. But he had a gentle voice and seemed sincerely concerned with my frustrations.

I asked him about organ donation by anencephalics, and was it really true that it was against the law. I asked him if there were any sick babies there at Children's Hospital that needed transplants. The image of the woman in the grocery store and her sick baby floated through my mind.

He very reluctantly agreed with me, saying that there were babies right there in the hospital that needed organs, and that the organs of the baby I was carrying were needed desperately. He went on to say how tragic this situation was. He said I wasn't the first one to ask to do this, and it was unfortunate that there wasn't a way the law could set aside certain restrictions for anencephalic donors. To do so, however, would require some other way of determining brain death, since these infants were brain absent.

Feeling somewhat encouraged, I asked him if there was a way it could be done.

He said there had to be way, as long as there were doctors out there who were willing to try. Certainly there were parents out there who fully understood the condition and saw organ donation as a way to bring some meaning to their child's brief life. He told me about an organ procurement agency called SCOPPC; it stood for Southern California Organ Procurement and Preservation Center. It was founded by Dr. Robert Mendez of St. Vincent's Hospital. He wasn't sure if they could help me, but at least they might have some more answers for me. He wished me good luck and asked me to keep him informed about the situation.

"Please take care of yourself and try not to get your hopes too high," he cautioned before he hung up the phone, "just in case there's a let down."

Dr. Murphree had offered me a ray of hope. I knew the next step was to call these SCOPPC people. If anyone could understand what I was trying to do, it would be them. I'm sure they knew how important it was to find new organ donors, and at the very least they would be sympathetic to my idea.

I dialed the number that Dr. Murphree had given me. A woman by the name of Joanna Salamandra answered the phone. I cut straight to the chase.

"My name is Brenda Winner, and I'm six months pregnant with an anencephalic infant. My husband and I were interested in donating the infant's organs for transplantation after it is born. Dr. Lynn Murphree from Children's Hospital gave me this number and said to ask for Dr. Mendez. Dr. Murphree said that he might be able to help me."

Joanna answered that she was sorry, but Dr. Mendez was not available. She had a kind and sincere voice and seemed to genuinely care about our situation, but she said that what we wanted to do was illegal. I asked her if she agreed that the law should be changed. She replied that yes, the law should read differently for anencephalics, but as far as she knew it had never been done. She mentioned that a doctor in Europe had successfully performed a transplant using a live anencephalic donor, but he was brought up on murder charges. The doctor saved the life of a little girl, but that didn't matter to the authorities. By removing the heart of the anencephalic, he was considered guilty of murder. The dignity of the anencephalic infant was somehow taken away.

Again, I was amazed that so many people saw it that way. I told Joanna that I thought it was ridiculous that people actually believed that donating the heart of an anencephalic infant to save another baby's life destroyed the donor's dignity. Wouldn't saving another baby's life add meaning to the donor's brief life on this planet? All this bullshit was making me more determined than ever to get across my point, and I'm sure the frustration was beginning to show in my voice.

Joanna was sympathetic but could offer me no consolation. She said that Dr. Mendez was only human like everyone else, and that he could not perform miracles. All we could hope for now was a quick death for our infant before the organs began to atrophy. The recipient would have to be close by, because they couldn't even start looking for a recipient until brain death occurred, even if they were aware of the condition of the baby and death was inevitable.

All of this was making me more angry and confused. Joanna mentioned that other parents had attempted to do the same thing in the past but were stopped by the Right-to-Life. They felt that organ donation interfered with the baby's right to die with dignity.

I couldn't believe it. Why was the Right-to-Life involved in this? After all, I wasn't having an abortion. Why should they care? I would think that they would approve of what I'm trying to do.

They fight like hell for the rights of unborn babies, and then they have no concern for babies who need transplants? The whole thing was amazing. I told Joanna I thought that people like that should just mind their own damn business. Let the parents and doctors decide when the rights of their baby are being violated. We don't need some sanctimonious band of hypocrites telling us parents what is in our baby's best interest. Don't these people realize what they're doing? They're letting hundreds of babies die that might otherwise live! Why don't they call themselves the "Right-to-Deny-Life"? That would be more in step with their position!

Before I hung up the phone I assured Joanna that I was all right and not to worry about me. I think she sensed that I would be calling again.

As soon as Mike got home, I filled him in on all the amazing details of the day's conversations. He was just as surprised as I was that the Right-to-Life was involved. I asked him if he thought we were in the right on this or if we were trying to do something immoral or undignified.

"Well now," he answered, "how can that be? Sure a person has a right to die with dignity and respect. But doesn't that person also have a right to decide for himself what is dignified and respectful? And if that person can't decide for himself, shouldn't the family be the next in line to make the decision? If this baby suffered brain damage in a car accident wouldn't they come straight to us for a decision? People just assume that this baby would rather be left alone to die than try to help somebody else. I can't believe that our baby, if it had the capacity to think, would see us as immoral or undignified for wanting to save the life of another human being. In fact, I'm sure that our baby would be very proud of what we are trying to do."

Mike's words made perfect sense to me. Every person born on this Earth is entitled to their own spark of hope. Every person has a God given right to leave a positive legacy, if they can, of their time on this planet, no matter how brief or fleeting their life might be. The people who want to stop us from doing this thing aren't concerned with preserving anyone's rights. They just want to impose their own set of ideals and morals on the rest of us and leave it at that. They don't want to be disturbed by any of the dirty issues or complex situations that may result from their shortsighted point of view.

Why should it hit home with them? They're not facing what Mike and I are facing. All they really care about is that their tidy, orderly view of God in His Universe is threatened. If there's one thing religious zealots avoid like the plague it's difficult or troubling questions without any clear-cut answers. No, I am not going to be intimidated. I know that I'm right, and I am going to find a way to get this thing done!

CHAPTER V

The weekend gave me a good chance to put my thoughts together, and I decided to give Loma Linda another chance. Maybe if they sensed that I was more confident and better informed they wouldn't brush me off so easily. My call was forwarded to obstetrics. I told the person at the other end of the line that I was six months pregnant with an anencephalic fetus, and I wanted to speak to someone about a possible organ donation.

"Hello, my name is Dr. Sherman. How can I help you?" answered a woman's voice. She had a soft, but emotionless, voice. It was a voice like you would expect to hear on an answering machine or coming from a telephone operator. I could also tell from the tone of her voice that she already knew about me.

"I'm six months along with an anencephalic infant," I began, "and we have decided to carry the baby to term and donate its organs. Since our insurance won't cover us for an organ donation, I'd like to ask if we could call it even. You know, I'd deliver there, since you have the facilities. You can use the baby's organs, and we would just walk away. We wouldn't have to know where the organs went unless it's necessary for health purposes."

"I'm very sorry to hear about your baby," Dr. Sherman answered, "but I'm afraid what you ask is impossible. For one thing, you can't just walk in and deliver. Not just anyone can walk into Loma Linda Hospital, Mrs. Winner."

I felt my throat tense up with indignation. This woman definitely was patronizing me.

"As far as donating the organs," she continued, "we would have to wait for the baby to die if it is alive. If it is stillborn, the organs are not any good."

"But the baby will die anyway," I interrupted, "and we as the parents have decided that we want this done. Since the organs will not be usable after the baby dies, isn't better to remove the organs at birth?"

"But to do that, Mrs. Winner, would make the organ removal the ultimate cause of death, and that is against the law. There isn't a doctor in the world that would do this."

"What about in the case of life and death?" I asked.

"Well, that would depend on the circumstances."

"What kind of circumstances?"

"I don't know, Mrs. Winner. There are all sorts of tests that must be done in organ donation. There is a biological one, which tests the tissues to see whether they match, and then there is the geographical test that determines which part of the country the donor and recipient live in. These all take time."

"I'm giving you three months!" I answered. "I know the statistics. What about the sick babies who need transplants? Why aren't they considered more important? What is the point in carrying this baby to term if we can only wait for it to die and then bury it?"

"You have got to realize that until brain death occurs, we cannot remove the organs."

"Wait!" I quipped. "How do you determined brain death in an infant that is brain absent?"

"There is a brain stem and..., " Dr. Sherman tried to explain.

"I know. I know all about the brain stem, but it doesn't make any sense."

"Well, with the absence of the neocortex, or the top brain," Dr. Sherman continued, "they lack the intelligence to breathe, thus causing the brain stem to deteriorate. They eventually reach death by asphyxiation or by starvation. Usually respiratory failure occurs first."

Dr. Sherman's description conjured up horrible images in my head. I envisioned this pathetic little baby desperately gasping for air and unable to swallow with Mike and me standing by powerless and helpless. How can they call that dignified?

"What does 'asphyxiation' mean?" I asked her. "Does it mean choking?"

"Well, yes," she answered.

"That's painful, right?" I interjected.

"Well we don't know if the babies can actually feel pain. The pain center is in the neocortex, which is missing in anencephalics. We assume they don't know that pain hurts, as we do."

"What? There is something wrong here!"

"We know what you are saying, Mrs. Winner. We agree with you, the organs are needed, but our hands are tied. There are ethicists and doctors and lawyers who will fight this attempt. The Right-to-Life will call it fetal abuse and inhumane. There isn't a doctor in the world who will help you."

"Why do all those other people have to be involved?" I argued. "No one could say a damn thing if I chose to abort this baby. We are the ones who decide whether to carry this baby to term or not. Why can't we be the ones who decide whether or not the organs are donated? If I'm responsible for my baby's life, why can't I decide what to do with the organs after my baby's death?"

"I understand, but comfort care is all we can offer," she answered.

"Well comfort care stinks, and I won't let it happen to my baby!" I said. A brief pause entered the conversation before Dr. Sherman continued.

"Mrs. Winner, there is nothing you can do before you deliver. You should put this tragedy behind you and have another baby as soon as you can. Just try to forget about this."

"Yeah, right. I should pretend like this never happened. Now that's really dignified. Goodbye." I hung up the phone and went to play with Amanda.

My conversation with Dr. Sherman was still haunting me, but I did my best not to let on in front of Amanda. The part about whether anencephalics could feel any pain stuck with me in particular. Even Dr. Sherman admitted that no one knew for sure whether they could feel pain. I just couldn't stand it knowing that my baby was in excruciating pain and not be able to do anything about it. How can anyone say it's immoral to stop something like that?

The more I thought about it, the more the idea of removing the organs at birth seemed like the most humane choice possible. Dr. Sherman's description of how anencephalics normally die under comfort care had me thoroughly, if quietly, horrified. Up to now I have been so concerned with saving other people's babies that I haven't really given much thought to the suffering that might await my own child. Organ donation at birth is the best way to insure that my baby won't have to go through days of the unspeakable suffering that Dr. Sherman described to me. I was beginning to realize that the main reason I was in this thing wasn't to martyr my baby in the name of the organ transplant industry, but to protect my baby from the horrors of a slow and painful death.

The next day I called SCOPPC. Joanna answered the call. I'm sure she sensed the frustration in my voice because the first thing she asked was whether I was OK. I told her about my conversation with Sherman. She didn't seem surprised by the doctor's response to my ideas. She explained that it's really the brain death law that we're up against, not any individual doctor.

"What does brain death have to do with it?" I pleaded. I was starting to feel like a broken record player. "The baby is brain absent. How can it not be brain dead?"

Joanna must have felt my growing anger and tried to calm me down. Then she told me that we were not the first couple to try this, that there were others before us.

That news sent me into a tirade, making me even angrier.

"What is it going to take to get through to these people?" I started ranting. "Why can't people just butt out and mind their own business? Why are they forcing decisions like this on the doctors and parents? If I went out today and had this baby aborted, these people wouldn't even have the right to know about it, let alone the right to force this kind of decision on me!"

Joanna could only offer me patience, sympathy, and a few kind refrains of "I know, I know...."

Having been drained from my outburst to Joanna, I tried to calm down and shift the topic of conversation.

"Are they sure that the organs of anencephalic babies are good at birth?" I asked her in a more sedate tone of voice. After all, it wasn't Joanna's fault that this was happening. Deep inside it was beginning to sink in how difficult it was going to be to donate our baby's organs. Still I felt the need to keep trying.

She replied that the organs were probably good, although each individual case is different. It would depend on the size of the baby, but more likely than not the baby's organs are in good condition. I reminded her of the many babies in need that I encountered in my telephone quest to find answers. What about them? Why don't their parents come out and ask for donors?

"What if I offered my baby's organs to them directly?" I asked her. "Would they turn me down?"

Joanna explained that to advertise or solicit like that would be unfair to the parents of babies who need transplants. It would only give them false hope, since they could not legally accept my offer.

I paused for a moment to consider Joanna's words. I guess I saw her point. I was finished pounding on the table for the day. I told Joanna goodbye. Mike would be home soon.

Mike and I spent most of that evening just talking. I had to feel sure that, if the baby could talk to us, it would assure us that we were doing the right thing. It seemed silly, but we spent a lot of the evening talking to my belly and the baby it held inside. It was like we were trying to get to know each other better or at least let our child know what kind of people its parents really were.

The first thing I did the next day was call SCOPPC back. A woman named Michelle Flaherty answered this time. I asked for Joanna, but she was out in the field and was unavailable. Michelle mentioned that she and Joanna were friends, and that Joanna had told her about my situation.

She went on to tell me the story of her second baby, one she lost very shortly after it was born. He had hypo-plastic lungs, a condition where the lungs don't develop completely. I could sense the pain in her voice as she described how she got pregnant again right away, without taking the time to grieve for her loss. Because she got pregnant right away and didn't take that extra time, she never got over the baby's death.

"Don't ever forget about this baby," she told me. "It did exist, and you have a permanent bond there with it. Give yourself enough time to get over this tragedy."

Michelle's story made me think again how important this baby was to me, even if it wasn't going to live. I was more determined than ever to carry on my quest. I wasn't going to put this baby behind me like everyone insisted I should. And there was no way that getting pregnant again right away was going to fill the void. I may be stuck with one tragedy, but I couldn't sit still without trying to use our tragedy to keep yet another one from happening. Most of all I couldn't bear the thought of my child being left to suffer a slow and agonizing death just so the medical community, and everyone else for that matter, could avoid any appearance of being responsible for my baby's death. But causing my baby's death by doing nothing is just as bad, if not worse, than causing it by harvesting the organs. Death by neglect is just a lower profile way to commit murder, if you can consider ending the life of someone who has no brain as murder. But nobody seems to get that. Somehow everyone thinks that committing murder by neglect is the only moral thing to do. How can you call that rational?

Later I was telling Mike about my conversation with Michelle. Mike was very supportive and pleased with my strong position, and he agreed with me on it wholeheartedly. He also thanked me for being such a thoughtful and caring person to fight so hard to save the life of a total stranger. In the middle of our conversation the baby started moving inside me, distorting my belly in a gentle rolling motion. It was incredible. I could actually make out the outline of a little foot pushing out against my stomach wall. It was an inspiring display, as if the baby understood our conversation and was making its approval known.

I called Joanna again the next day. We discussed the opposition, who they were, and their arguments against anencephalic organ donors. No matter how many times their position was explained to me, I simply could not understand it, just as I guess they could never understand my side of the argument. I continued to be amazed that the Right-to-Life was so firmly against what I was trying to do. They claim that the baby's right to die with dignity and respect would be disregarded. I claim that there is nothing more dignified or respectful of human life than saving another human life.

I asked Joanna if she thought it would help if I talked to the Right-to-Life directly. She said that it probably wouldn't help. I decided to try anyway.

After calling information, I dialed the number for the Pasadena Chapter of the Right-to-Life. An older woman answered. I told her who I was and asked if they had any information on their stand against anencephalic organ donation. She was very nice and said she was sorry, but what was that again and could I spell it for her. After explaining my situation and spelling "anencephaly" for her, I mentioned that I was five and half months pregnant and that my husband and I had decided to donate the baby's organs at birth.

She said that she was sorry, but at the moment she was unaware of their position. She asked me if I could call back. By now I was starting to get irritated, but I told her politely that I would call back. As I hung up the phone, I started to really feel hot under the collar. Here was a group who was determined to stop something they didn't even know how to spell! They had better have some more information when I call back. I felt like telling that lady "put up or shut up." But I knew that would have been rude and inappropriate.

I immediately called Joanna back and told her what happened. Joanna tried to calm me down, and she reminded me of the importance of taking care of my health first. She always seemed genuinely concerned about my well being. I asked her if she knew of anyone else who would oppose us, and she told me there were some politicians and lawmakers, but basically they were uninformed. It was one of those things that, unless it hit home with them, people would not understand. She suggested that I might write to my congressman or representative if I thought the laws were unfair.

Later I called back the Right-to-Life. This time a man answered the phone. He didn't offer me his name. When I told him I called previously about anencephaly and their policy on organ donation, he immediately acted as if he was an expert on the subject. He said the life of an anencephalic infant could not be sacrificed, short as it may be, even to save the life of another.

This man went on into a speech about how cruel it was to sit and wait for death to occur just to benefit someone else. I agreed and said that was why we wanted to remove the organs at birth, so we wouldn't have to wait for death to occur. Even if we didn't want to donate the organs, we didn't feel that it was fair to just set these babies aside and wait for them to die.

The man's voice turned indignant. He asked if I knew that what we wanted to do was called murder. He started acting like I was some kind of inhumane monster trying to snatch away innocent little babies from their parents to drag down with me during my fiery descent into hell.

"No doctor anywhere is going to cut up a baby for you and give its organs away," he snapped. "Could you actually bring yourself to do such a horrible thing?"

"Yes," I replied, "I could do it if I had the necessary medical qualifications. If there was a baby out there in need of an organ transplant, I would do it in a New York minute. What on Earth makes you think that it's moral to let two babies die when one might live?"

I must have hit a nerve because the man on the phone then came totally off the wall.

"In the eyes of the Church," he said, "and those who believe in reincarnation, it is wrong to interfere with God's way. When we die we should have all of our body parts intact, in order to evolve spiritually. If we believe in reincarnation, we have to return with what we are created with!"

"You're nuts, mister! Reincarnation has nothing to do with body parts! Reincarnation deals with our souls," I answered. But with that he refused to argue with me any longer. He said goodbye and hung up the phone. This had been my most astonishing phone conversation yet. I felt like I just showed up at a gunfight at the O.K. Corral with a popgun and a penknife.

I was beginning to realize that the people I was up against weren't rational. They weren't interested in logic or the facts or the real issues. They were only interested in prevailing their own gut emotional reactions. To them Mike and I are baby killers trying to peddle fresh human organs to the highest bidder on the nearest street corner.

After all it's much easier to point fingers at someone you don't know than it is to think for yourself or delve into complex moral issues. To them having the loudest voice was tantamount to having the most righteous one. How can you have an intelligent conversation with someone like that? But then this was just one individual, and I guess it was unfair to hold the entire Right-to-Life movement accountable for the statements of one idiot in their ranks. But I wondered how many more like him were out there, and what if people really believed what they had to say? Donating our baby's organs was going to be even harder than I ever expected.

I called Joanna back and told her about my phone conversation with the Right-to-Lifer. Not wanting to burden her with any more of my frustrations with the Right-to-Life, I asked her about the survival statistics for babies awaiting organ transplants. She told me that about five hundred babies a year need heart transplants, and about five hundred more a year are waiting for liver, kidney, or lung transplants. Somewhere between 40 percent to 70 percent of these babies die while they are waiting for organs to become available. I told Joanna how odd I thought it was that no one even considered the potential recipients in the overall moral equation. It was almost like people were pretending that they didn't even exist. I asked her how organs for transplantation were obtained from other types of organ donors.

Joanna explained that even if the death of an individual was deemed imminent, the blood and tissue types of the prospective donor could not be determined until the donor was confirmed to be brain dead. If it was done sooner, she continued, it might be construed that someone was rushing along the person's death in order to provide a fresh supply of transplantable organs. Many people feared the possibility that organs would be taken before the death of the donor was an absolute certainty. Also, the dignity of the donor must be assured.

Once death occurred, she told me, the organ procurement team would remove the organs and rush them to wherever they are needed. After that, all they could do was hope that a proper match with a recipient could be found quickly.

Joanna told me that there was more to people's fears than just preserving the donor's dignity. Many people feared what they called the "slippery slope" effect. If organs were allowed to be taken from anencephalics while they were still technically alive, it might set a precedent for even more latitude to be taken with other types of donors. People feared that it might not stop with just anencephalics. It might lead to other non-terminal patients being killed for their organs or babies being bred for "spare parts."

My conversation with Joanna left me very thoughtful. I had learned so much from her. I guess I understood better now what it was that people were so afraid of. After all, up until I found myself in this situation, I might have agreed with them. No one wanted to bring back Nazi Germany and allow the Dr. Frankensteins of the world to roam the night hunting for fresh organs.

But somehow I knew that most people were missing the whole story here. This wasn't one of those marginal situations where there was a lot of gray area or uncertainty. We weren't talking about babies that might die and then again might not. These were babies that had absolutely no chance of survival: nada, zip, nil. We're talking about contradictions in the law. Sure, it's perfectly legal, Mrs. Winner, to have your baby chopped up into little pieces, as long as you do it before the baby is born and the organs don't benefit anyone. Sure, Mrs. Winner, your baby has no brain, but the law says we still have to wait for the brain to die, even though we're not quite sure whether or not it even exists. Most of all, if you believe taking organs from anencephalics would inevitably land you on a slippery slope, then you have to conclude that these babies *must* be kept on life support in order to extend

44

their lives as long as humanly possible. Otherwise won't all the other patients on life support be at risk? After all if we deny anencephalics life support, won't we be in imminent danger of ripping the respirators off every unconscious patient in the nation? What hogwash!

I kept thinking about the sick babies who need organ transplants. I kept thinking how I hated the idea of comfort care and the death vigil that goes with it. Why should my baby suffer like that? What does it prove? I couldn't stop being angry about that.

I began to wonder what the babies who need transplants look like. I felt the baby kick again inside me. I decided that I had to see them for myself. I got out the Thomas Guide map book and began to look for Children's Hospital. I didn't tell Mike where I was going. He had enough on his mind without worrying any more about me.

It was a hot and sweaty day outside, and I had a hell of time finding Children's Hospital after I got off the freeway. Eventually I made my way in the front door and hopped on an elevator up to the Neonatal Intensive Care Unit. As the elevator doors opened, I could see the hustle and bustle of nurses, doctors, and parents wandering in all directions. In the background I could hear the steady, but weak, din of crying and whimpering babies.

Although the babies were isolated in a separate room, and the noise was muffled by the walls and glass partitions, the sound of it all still seemed deafening to me. I walked by two women who were staring into the glass panel separating the hallway from the nursery. One of the women's eyes were all red, like she had been crying. I overheard her say to the other woman that the doctor told her that she might be able to take her baby home tomorrow. The medication seemed to be working this time, she said. Her voice had a monotonous tone, like she had heard this same news many times before. It was as if she didn't really believe her own words, but had to keep repeating them in order to convince herself that her baby was going to be OK.

I looked at her baby on the other side of the glass. It couldn't have been more than a month old. The poor thing looked all yellow and was no larger than the size of my hand. It had a very frail and hoarse little cry, as if it was too weak and too small to fully express its agony. It made me feel terrible to look at a little baby in pain like that. I thought of saying something to the two women standing next to me, but what could I say? Instead I continued to walk around, looking at all these teeny tiny babies hooked up to these massive machines. I was beginning to think that Mike and I were the lucky ones. I noticed a few couples standing in the hallway, oblivious to everything that wasn't on the other side of the glass panel. I wanted to scream out to all of them "Hey, my baby was sent here to save your baby!" but I resisted. Under the circumstances that would have been a terribly cruel thing to say.

One of the nurses in the intensive care unit started checking me out. She came up to me and gave me the classic "Can I help you?" once over. I told her that I was waiting for a friend. She asked me if I minded waiting outside. This was the intensive care unit and only family members were allowed on this floor. I complied, but I took a long last look at one of the couples in the hallway as I walked out. I understood now why these people weren't out campaigning to change the organ donor laws. They already had too many problems of their own to contend with.

The next day I told Joanna about my little excursion. She seemed shocked that I went to so much trouble just to see those poor babies. She was beginning to realize how serious I really was about this thing. Then she dropped a bombshell on me. Joanna told me about a doctor at the University of Southern California named Dr. Lawrence Platt. His specialty was perinatology, or the study of the fetus while it is still in the womb. She thought that maybe he would talk to us, and he might even be able to help us. He had spent the last two years campaigning to make organ donation at birth legal for anencephalic infants. He lectured on the subject all over the country and was lobbying in Congress and state legislatures and anywhere else he could get people to listen. My heart began to pound as I wrote down Dr. Platt's phone number.

CHAPTER VI

I called Dr. Platt's office almost immediately. I was anxious and a little scared. I finally got through to his nurse. She told me that the doctor wasn't available, but he would return my call. The waiting was awful. I stared at the phone trying to make it ring with nothing but pure will power and raw hope.

Dr. Platt returned my call later that same day. I was instantly uplifted. He told me that he had spoken with Joanna, and he would be glad to hear out the circumstances of our situation. He mentioned that he was becoming an expert in the area of anencephalic organ donors. He agreed that to remove the organs at birth was the best chance for the organs to be successfully transplanted, and the moral decision should belong to the parents.

Dr. Platt then told me the story of Gail and Greg Merell. They discovered that Gail was carrying an anencephalic fetus in 1982. Although she was in her eighth month of pregnancy, they chose to have the baby taken early with hopes of donating the organs to a needy transplant recipient. They too came up against the brain death law, among other obstacles. They fought hard, but in the end they didn't succeed in donating their baby's organs. But they felt the same way as Mike and I did — that donating the organs of their doomed baby would give their loss greater meaning.

Dr. Platt went on to tell me about his efforts to change the brain death laws to allow organ donation by anencephalics. He agreed that there was nothing undignified or disrespectful for parents to donate their baby's organs in such a situation, and that the decision should be theirs alone to make. His feelings were very strong on the issue, and he had gathered and presented all the medical facts to the politicians in Washington, D.C. and elsewhere. Although many found his arguments convincing, no one was willing to take action. He needed someone like us — parents who wanted to donate their baby's organs and were willing to come forward publicly to express their views.

I was really starting to get excited. This was the man I was trying to reach all along. I just didn't know where to find him. He needed a willing party, someone who obviously was not coerced to come forward by an outsider. He needed someone who wasn't afraid to confront the issues and speak out on them. I finally found someone in the medical community who was on my side. This was perfect. No advertising necessary here, Dr. Platt. You have yourself two willing parents — in the flesh. Just let me at 'em, Doctor!

"I have been in contact with ABC Nightline," Dr. Platt told me, "and they are interested in the subject. Would you be willing to talk to a reporter?"

"I guess so. What about?" I answered.

"Just about yourselves and your situation," he reassured me. "It's going to take people like you to tell other people like you that this decision was one you made on your own. It is important that people know you were not coerced, and you are fully educated on the subject. People don't want to hear what doctors have to say on the issue, since they all assume that we are only after more money. It's unfortunate that the care we put into saving babies goes unnoticed in transplant situations. But when you talk about transplants and suggest using babies as donors, a lot of fears and questions get raised immediately."

Dr. Platt was anxious to see us as soon as possible and perform a fetoscopy examination of the baby firsthand. I made an appointment to see him on September 21, but because of his busy schedule, it had to be canceled. It seemed like it was going to be forever until we could get in to see him. In the meantime, I went in to see Dr. Suvannee for a checkup. I asked her what fetoscopy was. She explained that fetoscopy is a procedure where they enter the uterus with a miniature camera to get a closer look at the baby's internal organs. She mentioned that she had spoken with Dr. Platt on the phone and wished me good luck. She said that it was sometimes a risky procedure, but I had nothing to worry about.

"Dr. Platt is very good at what he does," she told me.

I tried to hold onto my hopes and keep a positive outlook, but time seemed to pass ever more slowly. There were so many times when depression would set in. Every time I felt the baby moving inside me, however, I seemed to temporarily snap out of it. It was as though the baby was reaffirming my commitment not to give up. After all, the baby wasn't giving up on me, so why should I give up on it? And why should I give up on that baby out there who needs our help?

I was at a particularly low point when Smily and Christi came by for a visit. It was not long after the Whittier Narrows earthquake, on October 1. Arcadia is not far from Whittier, and this shaker was a little too close to home for comfort. My nerves and my patience were definitely frazzled. As we loafed around and watched TV, an item came on the news about a baby, referred to by the press as Baby Paul, who had been born the night before. He was the first infant to ever survive a heart transplant. Christi became hysterical.

"Get to the phone and find out where the heart came from!" she demanded. "Don't just sit there! Call someone! Find out!" she kept insisting.

I immediately called Dr. Platt, and he unloaded another bombshell on me. The organ donor was anencephalic! I was positively stunned. He said that he would try to get more information for me and would call me back as soon as possible.

I hung up and waited for more information to come onto the TV news. Sure enough, they did mention that the donor was anencephalic, but all the details were about the recipient baby. Christi was getting so excited that sparks were practically flying off her. I was getting charged up just watching her. We had to find out what was going on here.

Dr. Platt called me back not long afterwards and said that the donor had met brain death with the help of a respirator.

"Could that be done?" I asked.

"Apparently so," Dr. Platt answered. "Maybe there is a difference in the law in Canada. That is where the procedure was done."

Dr. Platt asked if I would be willing to go to Canada, if it proved necessary.

49

"Yes, anything!" was my reply.

As the day wore on, the initial shock of the news started to wear off somewhat. I began to collect more and more information on the situation. There were special circumstances in this case. Baby Paul was discovered to have hypo-plastic left heart syndrome while he was still in the womb. The left side of his heart was severely underdeveloped. The donor baby, Baby Gabrielle, was diagnosed as anencephalic while still in the womb, and her parents had insisted that the organs be donated for transplantation. After her birth, she was watched carefully for signs of distress and was placed on a respirator to ensure that her organs were properly oxygenated. Baby Paul was then taken by C-section. Shortly after being placed on a respirator, Baby Gabrielle was determined to be brain dead, and her heart was immediately transplanted into Baby Paul.

As I found out more about Baby Paul my frustration started to build again. Why were we having such a hard time when this type of thing was already being done? What was the big deal? Now we have proof that no one can deny. Baby Paul is alive only because the heart was allowed to be taken from Baby Gabrielle before her organs atrophied. Who can deny the good brought about by a thing like this? Who can say that it is immoral for this baby to still be alive? Yet that is exactly what people are saying to us; we don't have the right to donate our baby's organs, even if other lives are spared. They act like we are criminals just because we care about saving another baby's life, and we don't want our own baby to suffer needlessly. The hypocrisies and inconsistencies behind this whole situation still staggered me.

After venting my frustration on the phone to Dr. Platt, he guaranteed me he would get to the bottom of the Baby Paul situation. I told him that if time was a factor, I was giving them almost three months to prepare. Dr. Platt brought up the ABC Nightline interview again and asked me if we were willing to talk about our predicament on TV.

"Absolutely!" I told him.

My latest conversation with Dr. Platt started me thinking about the news media. How would they handle the issue? How would it go over with the general public? How many people out there even know what anencephaly is? Everyone I've told about it so far didn't know what the hell I was talking about. Even my own mother, who raised eight children of her own, had never heard of it. My guess is that the public was totally unaware of these poor doomed babies and was uneducated about the lives they could save. I wondered how many mothers of anencephalics out there would agree with my position once they had all the facts.

Eventually I got hold of a newspaper article put out by the New York Times wire service on Baby Paul. I was struck by the fact that the parents had insisted that their infant's organs be used, and that the mother's wish to donate her infant's organs was "considered paramount." The article also mentioned a conference held in Ontario, Canada, the previous January in which a consensus was reached among those who attended that, in the presence of consenting parents, it was ethical to offer the anencephalic baby life support. I was starting to feel good again. Maybe our idea wasn't so unreasonable after all.

Then came the down side of the article. Some doctor at the University of California, San Francisco said that "it has not been deemed ethical to use anencephalic infants as transplant donors in North America because, lacking brains, they do not meet strict criteria for brain death and, thus, are not considered legally dead." I started getting angry again. I scribbled my responses to each negative argument in the margins and between the lines of the newspaper article.

Finally the day of our appointment with Dr. Platt arrived. His office was located at the LA County/USC Medical Center. The first thing he did was give me an ultrasound examination, and some of his medical students were present to watch. Afterwards we talked in his office. He was pleased with the condition of the baby, and he told us that the organs looked large and healthy. Fetoscopy was not necessary. He was careful not to make us any promises, but there was something in his manner and style that made me feel confident. I was convinced that we finally had a chance of successfully donating our baby's organs.

I asked Dr. Platt if USC would go along with our plan to donate the baby's organs. He said it didn't seem likely, since USC was a county hospital and wasn't equipped for such a procedure. He mentioned Loma Linda Hospital. I told him that I had already been in contact with them, and that their response had been very negative. I was not enthusiastic about getting involved with them.

Dr. Platt listened carefully to my complaints about Loma Linda, but he countered that their success rate with intensive care cases was very high. He also told us that Loma Linda was a learning institution, and as such would be a good place to test new or experimental procedures. I still pushed for him to try another hospital first.

Several days later I noticed an article in the Los Angeles Times about Dr. Leonard Bailey — the doctor at Loma Linda who transplanted a baboon heart into Baby Faye several years back. In the article Dr. Bailey backed off on the procedures used to save Baby Paul. He said there were no circumstances where he would remove organs from a moving crying baby, even if it was anencephalic. The article left me feeling appalled. Our hopes that we finally had found a way to donate our baby's organs once again seemed to be dashed up against the rocks. How could he say those things, the patriarch of Loma Linda medical science, after seeing so many babies die from a lack of transplantable organs? How can someone transplant a baboon heart into a human baby, but then turn down the perfect human donor?

I was so incensed that I picked up the phone and called the Pasadena Star News. As soon as someone picked up the phone I started into a rage.

"How come they're transplanting baboon hearts into live human babies," I shouted, "yet I have a perfect organ donor right here inside me that nobody wants."

My phone call was transferred to a staff writer by the name of Selwyn Eiber. I abruptly repeated my tirade for him.

"Yes, my name is Brenda Winner, and I am carrying an anencephalic infant who is doomed to die at birth. We want to donate the organs, but nobody wants them!" I ranted.

The reporter was taken aback at first, but then he started asking me about the details. How far along was I? How did I find out the baby was anencephalic? After he asked me a few more questions, we set up a time for an interview.

After I hung up the phone, I realized that I had just done a very rash and impulsive thing. I didn't talk it over with Dr. Platt, or even Mike, before I called. I felt little anxious about what I might be letting myself in for. But it was too late now. Later, after I told Mike about the upcoming interview, he agreed with me that it was the right thing to do.

"We'll just have to wait and see what happens," he told me.

CHAPTER VII

When the reporter and photographer arrived at our apartment, they were very nice and very pleasant. They also seemed to be sympathetic to our situation. The reporter had a quiet and soft-spoken manner — a trait that surprised me in a newspaperman. Somehow I never thought of reporters as likable and respectable, but that certainly was the impression this one gave to me. He seemed a little shocked at how seriously I was taking things and the number of facts I had collected to support my position. Still I felt comfortable telling my story to this man and the photographer who came with him. Somehow deep down inside I could tell they were going to present this thing sensitively in their newspaper.

Once we were settled and got down to business the first thing the reporter asked was where I got my information. I wanted to tell him all about Joanna and SCOPPC, but then I backed off a little. I was reluctant to mention them by name. They had enough controversy and fanatics to deal with without me adding to the situation. But he was interested in how I got my facts, and I mentioned that I had talked to an organ transplant procurement organization without giving any specifics. I told him that the head of the organization did not agree with our position, but that the girls working the phone lines were supportive and sympathetic. I explained to him the reason I thought the head of the transplant agency was so anxious to distance himself from us; the

Right-to-Life crowd was out there watching and waiting for something to protest.

"Well, let's start from the beginning," interjected the reporter. He seemed very interested in what I was saying, but as usual I was trying to feed him too much information too fast. In the process we had drifted off track.

He asked me for some basic facts. How was our name spelled? How many months along was I? When was I due?

"When did you first find out that the baby was...," he asked, struggling to pronounce the word "anencephalic."

Mike and I sounded out the two variations slowly for him, "An-en-ce-pha-lic and an-en-ce-pha-ly."

"What is anencephaly?" he asked us. Even a professional writer was having trouble with this word.

"It's a zoological term," I explained. " 'An' means 'no' or 'without,' and 'encephaly' means 'brain.'"

We talked about how I found out I was carrying an anencephalic infant, and the whole ordeal of my ultrasound session in gory detail. He was very interested in what our first reaction was to the news. I told him that, of course, we were in shock, but we also wondered what it was that we did to cause this situation. I told him that since I had given up smoking, and drinking, and even putting gas in my own car, I thought I was going to have the perfect pregnancy. That was what made the news so shocking and hard to accept.

It seemed like the reporter couldn't get the words down on his pad fast enough. Was this story really that interesting, or was I just some obsessed pregnant woman absorbed in her own problems? But the reporter's apparent enthusiasm for our story was starting to make me feel more at ease. The mixed feelings I had earlier about doing the interview were now melting into a nice warm glow. I felt a quiet confidence that this newspaper interview was finally going to shake something loose out there.

I waited for another long pause so that the reporter could catch up again on his note taking. He feverishly flipped over to a fresh sheet of paper.

I told the reporter about our choice between the option to carry our baby to term or the option to abort. Since for us abortion was out of the question, both because of the moral issues and also the health risks involved, I explained how we came to decide to try to donate the baby's organs. He asked for more information about anencephaly and what causes the condition, and of course we could only tell him that nobody knows what causes it and that very little research was being done to determine the cause.

"It's like what my doctor says: 'When we don't know what it is, we blame it on environmental factors,'" I told him. "Some of the women have taken birth control pills, some of them haven't. Some of the women were drug users, some of them didn't use drugs."

"Is there like a foundation for anencephaly?" the reported quizzed.

"No," Mike and I answered in chorus.

"There's nothing for this," I added.

Mike echoed, "There's nothing at all...."

Once again I took over the conversation.

"In fact, the majority of these births are surprise births. That's why I feel we were so fortunate to find out ahead of time. We thought we were going to be able to simply make arrangements for the organs to be donated, then we found out that we were up against a brick wall with it. We cannot do anything until the baby is legally declared brain dead."

Another pause entered the conversation before I continued. We had gotten to the heavy part.

"Which is unfortunate, because the definition of brain death pertains to someone who has had severe trauma to the brain. In other words, it refers to somebody who has a brain. This child doesn't have a brain."

There I finally spelled it out. It all seemed so plain and simple. A brain cannot be both alive and absent at the same time. Why can't people get it? These people who say "what about the brain stem?" are missing the point. These babies are doomed with absolute 100% certainty. Anyone who says removing their organs is to ultimately be the cause of their death needs to recognize something. To simply keep these babies warm and dry and then wait helplessly for them to die on their own from starvation or asphyxiation is every bit as cruel of a process as removing their organs, maybe even more so. To claim that they are not brain dead is every bit as absurd as claiming that the stump left behind when lightning strikes a tree should be protected in the name of forest preservation.

Why is it so important to everybody that this baby inside me die for nothing? That's what I don't understand. If those precious

55

few days or hours that my baby would live if its organs were not taken are so important, then why aren't we prolonging those days and hours? Why not take heroic measures and spend billions of dollars to see that these infants live out every last millisecond medical science can possibly afford them? The answer you get, of course, is that it would be absurd to put these babies on machines; they'll die anyway. So if the very short life of an anencephalic baby isn't even worth prolonging, why must another baby die in order to prolong it?

I realized now that Mike and I were embroiled in a full scale war, a war for truth and a parent's right to decide the fate of their own child. Those who say that to simply remove the organs of anencephalics is wrong because it only benefits the recipient have never faced that longing feeling for their baby's suffering to end quickly. They won't know the importance of having their baby's brief existence come to some kind of meaningful end. They will only have their high moral standards and ethics to cling to — and of course the contradictions of their own shortsighted beliefs.

"Let's go back a little more," said the reporter. "The doctor told you that you could donate or you could abort. Were there any other choices?"

"Well, no, that was it," I answered. "She thought we could donate. So we went home and thought about it."

"Were those the only two options she gave you?" the reporter countered. "Did she give you any others?"

"What other one could there be?" I answered in a somewhat mystified tone. "Carry it full term or abort were the only options. I felt great physically, so why abort? I didn't want to get sick and be in the hospital for weeks and weeks...."

"The other alternative as far as a third choice, " Mike added, "as in A, B, or C, was to carry it full term, let it live for however long anencephalic babies live for, from a few hours to a few days, until it dies on its own."

"Is that the most that they would live for," the reporter said, "a few days?"

"Yes," Mike answered, "that would be the choice for C, and then what do you do? That's it. You know what the doctors tell the mothers and the fathers of these babies? That their baby was stillborn, so they won't have to deal with the fact that their baby is deformed."

"How did you hear that?" the reporter asked Mike.

A mini-surge of panic hit as I hoped that Mike wouldn't give out any names. I didn't need to alienate anybody in the medical profession by splattering confidences across the newspapers. Besides, it was one of those things that you hear about but can never prove if pressed about it.

"You keep talking to people," Mike answered, "that are concerned with this, doctors that know...."

"So friends told you, or different people told you, that this is what doctors will do," the reporter probed on.

"The doctors," Mike replied, "some of the doctors have told us this."

My mini-surge of panic went full-blown. Mike was about to spill the beans. I had to do something and quickly.

"Now honey, we don't want to say that," I interrupted, "because that could jeopardize our relationship with the doctors."

"Yeah, put that one off the record a little bit, please," Mike backpedaled.

"I mean," I took over, "if you have the baby, and it's born anencephalic, and the doctors tell you that the baby is not dead yet, but it's going to die in a few minutes, that can be very traumatizing to someone who has just had a baby. It was traumatizing to us at five and half months. But still, it's given me time to learn more about it so it will be easier for us to accept it. The majority of the births are surprise births; they don't know about the baby until after it is born. A lot of times the mothers and fathers just want to bury this baby, and organ donation is the farthest thing from their minds. And even if it was on their minds, they don't have much time to make a decision."

"I don't know how many other articles you've read," Mike interrupted.

"I haven't," replied the Star News reporter.

"Well, there's one article that we have," Mike continued, "that describes the whole thing to a tee. It tells you everything you ever wanted to know about it."

"Yes, I'd like to see it," the reporter answered.

"Another doctor," Mike went on, "who happens to be a big one on the moral issues of brain death and so forth, considers what happened with Baby Paul at Loma Linda getting the heart transplant to be a 'chess game' with the Canadian doctors. That's because the brain stem controls function, yet the brain controls everything else. And the term 'brain dead' is based upon respiratory function. That's the last thing they look for. If you're unable to breathe on your own, that's when you are brain dead."

I gave the reporter a copy of the newspaper article in the Arizona Republic about Baby Paul. I also showed him a letter that I wrote to the transplant coordinator for SCOPPC, although I asked him to keep their name off the record.

He asked me more about what Dr. Suvannee had told us about our options, and the events leading up to our decision to try to go ahead with organ donation. I told him about my phone conversations with Loma Linda, and how Dr. Suvannee had been supportive but had stopped short of telling us that Loma Linda was going to help us.

"You mean, she didn't want to say that yes, you can do all these things," he said, "because that might set you up for a big disappointment?"

"There's a big thing about the doctors making a lot of money off these transplants," I answered, "and coercion of people to donate organs is the big issue. That's something I really need to stress to you. Mike and I were not coerced by anybody to do this."

"It sounds more like you were dissuaded from doing it," the reporter replied.

"Yes, we were," I answered. "When I called Loma Linda, they told me to give up."

"When you say 'give up' you mean don't donate anything?"

"Yeah...just have the baby," I said, "and don't worry about it."

"Who told you this at Loma Linda?" the reporter inquired.

"I don't remember the names of the doctors I talked to. I called there, and one of them said to just have the baby and don't worry about it. By the time you deliver there's no way you can change the law on brain death anyway."

"What I did was I called and I said 'I want to know how I go about making sure that when I have this baby, you don't wait for brain death to occur, that you go ahead and remove the organs and let that be the cause of death.' And they told me that was called murder. The Right-to-Life people told me that it was called 'fetal abuse.' So I told them that I thought 'abuse' was what was happening to the babies kept waiting for organ transplants."

"Do you know whom you spoke with?" the reporter asked me.

"The first time I called I spoke to a woman. She didn't even know what anencephaly was. Another time I spoke to a man, I didn't get his name, and when I told them what I was intending to do, he all at once became an expert on the subject. Suddenly he really wanted to preserve that baby's 'rights.' That baby should be put on a machine; that was his thinking. I said there's no way this baby should be put on a machine. If that baby had a chance, then yes, I agree. Put it on a machine. But this is not a complete human being we are talking about here. This baby has no head, no skull. I've seen the pictures, and it's just a face. There is no forehead. There is no back to the skull. If the baby had a brain, and there was a chance that he could live — I'd put him on a machine in a New York minute. But the truth is this baby is doomed to die, no matter how you look at it. I just cannot see prolonging his life after birth any longer than necessary, especially when other lives are at stake."

"So OK, you spoke with the Right-to-Life, and they really told you no," interrupted the reporter.

"They didn't tell me no, they just told that the baby had to meet the brain death laws, and that these doctors make a lot of money doing organ transplants. That was one of their big things, was how much money these doctors were going to make on the transplants."

"Yet the two doctors you spoke with didn't want you to do it," answered the reporter.

"Right, partly because of these Right-to-Life people," I countered.

Suddenly the photographer, who had been silent up to this point, jumped into the conversation.

"Just one question I have out of curiosity. What authority does the Right-to-Life group have?" he interjected.

"Political ...," Mike answered.

"It's just political pressure that they are able to ...?" the photographer asked.

"I'm a democrat personally." Mike replied. "Ronny Reagan is republican, and he's anti-abortion. That's your Right-to-Life people right there in a nutshell."

"Some of the Right-to-Lifers thought that I should have had an abortion," I broke in.

"They told you that you should have an abortion?" asked the reporter in a disbelieving tone.

"They're so inconsistent!" added the photographer.

"They asked me 'Were you offered an abortion?'. I told them yes, and they said that in this case that was what I should have done. You see. That's what I can't understand about the Right-to-Life people. Where do they draw the line between religion and state? Who gives them so much power? I do know this from talking to one of their people. Two years ago there was a similar case where someone else found out that they were pregnant with an anencephalic baby. She wanted to donate the organs, and the Right-to-Life organization picketed her delivery!"

"One thing that I'm starting to realize," said the photographer, "is that power isn't given, it's taken. There isn't necessarily any good reason for people to have power. Power isn't based on right or education. It's if you can take it. And they have taken power."

"My point is that I respect what someone else believes," I said. "It may not be what I believe, but how dare you tell me what I can or cannot do when you don't even know what it is I'm talking about?"

"Exactly!" agreed the reporter.

"Michael and I feel that since we're responsible for this baby, the baby's rights also become our rights. What parent doesn't make decisions on behalf of their child? There are babies in Los Angeles that die every day because they can't get a liver, or kidney, or a heart. Here we are tossing away this baby's organs and the lives that those organs can save and for what? Because of some stupid law written by people who aren't even quite sure about what it is they are outlawing! I'll tell you, it isn't the parents that are missing the point on this issue."

"Their decision is the easier decision," the reporter answered. "The decision you're making is a hard decision. It's not a black and white decision. It's a very hard one to make."

"Well, they call themselves compassionate," I interrupted, "but how compassionate can you be if you go picket some poor expectant mother during her delivery? They just want to protect their 'moral' values that somehow are being threatened by this idea. They have no concept of the agony of a dying baby, or the dilemmas faced by a dying baby's parents. I don't think 'moral values' are at stake here at all. Saving lives is my moral standard. This baby is not going to live. I don't care how long you can keep it going on a machine, it's still going to die and soon. And because it's going to die, we want to give what we can — which is more life. There's no moral cost to this. We don't care how many doctors are benefiting from this. They might make a lot of money, but at least they're doing more than talking. They're saving lives."

"We don't want doctors to benefit from this. We want other children to benefit from this," Mike added.

"You started to say it, but let me ask you again," said the reporter, "the reasons why you're so strongly for donating the organs."

"Mainly because I found out all the other organs were normal and healthy on our baby," I answered, "and I found out how many babies die every day from having no liver or because they need other vital organs. It seems useless to me to just bury it and waste everything."

From that point on the interview became less and less of an interview and more of a supportive chat between old friends. I told them the story of how I found Dr. Platt. We told them how ABC Nightline was interested in an interview. I stressed how important it was that now that anencephaly was coming out of the closet and that we get beyond this brain death law. We need to start the process of saving lives. I told them about the doctor in England who was sent to prison for prematurely taking the organs from an anencephalic and transplanting them to save a little girl. But the conversation kept returning to Dr. Platt and the unique relationship we had developed with one another.

"When we first found out about it, and we came in contact with Dr. Platt," Mike said at one point, "you know it sounds odd, but he needed us as much as we needed him. We needed him because we feel strongly about this. We want to donate. He needed us because we are a potential breakthrough for his research, and we are not being coerced into doing this. We feel confident that this is the right thing to do."

"Is there anything else you're doing to try to get the laws changed?" the reporter said.

"Other than just educating people," I answered, "and explaining it to people we meet. Hardly anyone I've met has even heard of it."

"So you're just talking about it with your friends," he countered.

"Sure," Mike jumped in, "you go shopping at the supermarket and the girl at the checkout counter asks 'When are you due?'. What do you say to them? Well we turn right around and we tell them our baby is not going to live. Because our baby is not going to live, we want to be able to donate its organs."

61

"People don't realize how much trouble it is to do that," I added.

"We've been commended for this at our local supermarket right down the street," Mike continued. "They feel that we're very brave. That makes me feel fantastic inside."

"Yeah, earlier when I was in the car coming over here," offered the reporter. "I was thinking about you. That was the very word I thought of...brave. I think that what you are doing is very much the brave thing to do. That's maybe why some of these other people can't deal with the issues. Maybe they are not as brave. Maybe they don't realize that even though a decision is not an easy or a comfortable one, it still may be the right thing to do."

"We aren't the brave ones," I replied. "The brave people are the parents waiting for a transplant for their dying baby."

CHAPTER VIII

All in all, I was very pleased with how the Star News interview went. Deep down inside I now knew that it was the right thing to do. The baby was very active during the interview, perhaps because it felt my excitement, but now my belly seemed to relax and breathe a sigh of relief. I scrutinized the Star News every day as it came out, and then one day the following week the reporter called. He told me that our story was going to be on the front page of the Sunday paper. Wow! Front page coverage! I couldn't believe it.

When the Sunday edition of the Star News finally came out, I went out and bought a dozen copies. There on the front page was the beginning of a very powerful and moving article about our story. I could hardly believe that Mike and I were the main feature in the Sunday paper. Inside the paper there were two more full pages, complete with pictures. There was a large photo of Mike and me in the apartment. There was also a close up of me with the quotation "I believe this child was put on this Earth to help other children, like God asked us to do him a favor." attached in large type. Not bad, I thought to myself, to be quoted in a major Sunday paper. The article was great. It brought home our message that we were in this to help other children, and that we were very determined in our commitment to donate our baby's organs. It did not in the least portray us as bleeding hearts or sympathy seekers.

The next day we received two phone calls. The first came from a woman who wanted to give us one of her Persian kittens. The other was from a man who asked to talk to Mike. He said that he was very sorry for our loss, and he and his wife had gone through the same thing three years ago, but had never talked about it. He said he felt like he was the only one in the whole world who had fathered a freak. Mike talked to him for a long time. When they hung up, Mike mentioned how relieved the man seemed to finally talk about it with someone who could understand.

The following day the LA Times called and wanted to know if we would do an interview with their paper. I said sure. The interview was scheduled for the following week.

The reporter's name from the LA Times was Nikke Finke. She seemed as fascinated by our story as the guys from the Star News.

"Do you have any idea of how brave you are?" was one of the first things she asked.

I tried to play down the bravery thing, although I did tell her that many other people had told us how brave we were. General Custer had bravery on his side and look what happened to him. Besides I didn't want this story to focus on Mike or me. I wanted the story to focus on our baby and her connection to the babies who need the organ transplants. I didn't want to drum up public sympathy; we needed action! She went on to ask us many of the same questions as we had been asked by the Star News. How did I find out the baby was anencephalic? What was my first reaction to the news? How did I learn my facts? She seemed genuinely horrified by my story of the ultrasound session, but again I played down my personal feelings about the way I was treated.

I told the reporter about Baby Paul and how we found Dr. Platt. She was very curious about the details of Baby Paul's story, and what was now possible and what wasn't in the context of anencephalic organ donors. I told her the story of how Baby Gabrielle was kept on life support to preserve her organs until the transplant to Baby Paul could take place.

Much of what I told her was the same information as what I told the Star News. I told her how we blamed ourselves for what happened before we knew the whole story. I told her of my research on anencephaly at the library and how I got information talking to people on the phone. I explained the negative reactions we got when we first approached people about donating our baby's organs. I depicted most of the doctors I talked to as sympathetic but not very helpful. We also talked about the political agenda of the people opposed to using anencephalics as organ donors. I mentioned the doctor in England imprisoned for transplanting an anencephalic's organs to save a little girl. She also wanted to know where we were going from here, who were the doctors involved, and where was I going to deliver. She also asked what we would do if the Right-to-Life decided to protest our decision.

"Bring 'em on," Mike very quickly answered to that question. "We're ready."

Nikke was very supportive and told us any number of times how great it was that we came forward to tell our story. She also told us how clearly cut the issues seemed to be to her. I felt uplifted by her attitude and supportive remarks. It finally seemed like something big might happen. The LA Times article appeared on Friday, December 4, and was titled "A Matter of Death and Life." It was sincere and straightforward, like the Star News article, but reached a much larger audience. It avoided fact tossing aimed at intellectuals, politicians, and ethicists. Instead it was an up-close personal look at our situation and our desire to allow the organs to be taken from our baby and be donated at birth. Surprisingly, it even contained some conciliatory remarks quoted from Dr. Bailey. He suggested that they were looking into establishing a new medical protocol for anencephalic organ donors. I was feeling more encouraged than ever.

The day after the LA Times story hit the street all hell broke loose. The phone did not stop ringing the entire morning. NBC Evening News was the first to call. They wanted Mike and me to be on the evening newscast with Tom Brokaw. They came to pick me up at 8:00 A.M., and then we picked Mike up from work. We did the interview with reporter named Don Oliver in a hotel room near Knott's Berry Farm in Buena Park. Things were really starting to take off. I guessed that I was not the only one to be intrigued by this issue. People out there were starting to wake up and take notice.

The requests for interviews kept pouring in. McNeil/Leher News Hour called about doing a documentary film. NBC called again. This time it was a different affiliate station. Within that same day USA Today, the Today Show, CBS Radio, and the local CBS TV affiliate all called with requests for interviews. I was thrilled! I knew that something was going to break loose from all this, but I didn't expect to become awash in a flash flood of publicity. Things got so hectic that my best friend from high school, Jan, volunteered to come out from New Mexico to help me cope with the madness.

Having Jan there beside me was a lifesaver. She was almost like my personal secretary. She was also very supportive of my decision to bring the press in on this, even during the moments that I myself was having doubts. After all, I was very rash and hasty in making my decision, and I didn't take the time to think about how the press might present our story to the public. Now I was in up to my neck in media hype. Jan's presence seemed to calm me and reassure me that everything was going to be all right, and things would eventually get back to normal.

The interviews and the request for interviews never seemed to stop. We did at least one every day, sometimes two or three, sometimes more. Mike would come home and barely have time to clean up. We even did interviews without cleaning up. One day I spent six straight hours doing nothing but interviews. I was on a roll. I figured the more people we could get the word out to the better. The only interview I turned down was with People magazine. I guess it was because I felt they would try to sensationalize the story. They sent me a copy of their Baby Faye story (Dr. Bailey's patient who received a transplanted baboon heart at Loma Linda a few years before) in the mail. Right there on the magazine cover was Baby Faye's mother, clutching her baby and gushing with emotion.

I did not want to come off as a sympathy seeker. I was in this to spread a message, not to seek attention or compassion for myself. My message is a simple question. Why let two babies die when one might live? Brain death laws were meant to apply to people who have brains, and since the brain is absent in the case of anencephalics, a special definition of brain death is warranted. What is so complicated about it? Ultimately, don't the parents and their doctors have the responsibility to decide if organ donation is the right thing to do? I don't want people to be afraid to demand that right of responsibility. Don't be afraid to look through the hypocrisies and the legal mumbo-jumbo. Don't be afraid to speak out. After all we've been through, I wasn't going to let People magazine entomb my message deep within another one of their "sympathy sells" media circus side shows.

Soon I received calls from Time and Newsweek magazines requesting an interview. After thinking over which of the two newsmagazines could do the best job on the article, I decided to go with Time. I called them up and offered them my story. They were all too eager to accept. The first interview session lasted three hours, and we spent another two hours with them the next day. The reporter came off as being so sensitive and compassionate and involved that it was almost sickening. He made a point of saying over and over how badly he felt for us. I thought he was going to offer to adopt us. I kept emphasizing that Mike and I were trying to get past the emotional side of the issue. We were more concerned with doing the right thing rather than dwelling on our misfortune.

I guess the reporter didn't believe me. He kept saying real sappy things like "It's too bad good people like you have to go through this." and "You should try again because I know you two would make wonderful parents." and so on and so on. He even gave us his home phone number and told us to feel free to call him any time day or night. Although that kind of suck-up approach usually never works with me, I still thought that we had made some good points and the interview was worthwhile. I just hoped those points would come across OK in the setting of a national news magazine article.

Not long afterward we consented to another interview, this time with Newsweek, and pretty much went through the same routine. Every few days one the reporters would call and check in. They would ask if everything was OK and if we were having any luck finding a hospital that would take the organs. I wondered how long that kind of attention might last.

Another memorable interview was with National Public Radio. The interview went well, and they played back the final cut of the broadcast segment for me over the phone the next day. Although the story mainly featured my voice and a couple of quotes from Mike, they also included comments from Dr. Platt and some so-called "experts" in the field including one who supported us and one who opposed our position. Jan liked the reporter, a woman by the name of Wendy Kaufman. She told me that I should ask the reporter to help me write a book, but I was very negative. I didn't do all this so I could write a book, I told her. Someday, maybe, but not right now. It's the brain death law that I'm after.

I was feeling that fear of sensationalism again, and the thought of a book or a movie — at least at this point in time — made me cringe. Then I received a letter in the mail from a movie producer. She actually had the gall to offer me a check for one dollar in return for my publishing rights. One dollar! Now the creepy crawlers were really starting to come out of the woodwork.

The interviews continued on relentlessly. The media pressure on Loma Linda was reaching a crescendo, and for the time being the entire nation's attention seemed to turn to this little baby inside me. But even I did not expect the grand finale. Only a little over a week from when the LA Times article first hit the news stands, I got a call from Cable News Network. They told me that Loma Linda had announced a press conference, and it involved a new medical protocol for anencephalic organ donors. The man from CNN told me that about forty reporters were camping out in Dr. Sherman's office. They had been there for days, each of them taking turns at shoving a microphone in her face. Each one was demanding to know why Loma Linda could not honor our wishes and accept our baby's organs. He said that the word is out that they were finally caving in under the pressure, and they were going to announce a new protocol for organ donation by anencephalic infants.

The news took me completely by surprise. Suddenly, I realized that Mike and I might have just won a major victory. Me, a simple housewife, I had made the mighty organ transplant community listen and respond to me. But what had we really won? I needed to talk to Dr. Platt before I decided on an answer to that question.

I immediately called Dr. Platt and asked him about the details of the new protocol. The news, it seemed, was not without a down side. The protocol did not allow organ removal at birth, which was what Mike and I originally requested. The baby would be put on a respirator immediately after birth until it met the criteria for brain death. The other drawback was I had to deal with Loma Linda. Up to now my experiences with them had left me feeling lukewarm at best. After all, wasn't it Dr. Sherman who told me that "There isn't doctor in the entire world who will help you"? Now all of a sudden she's going to be our number one benefactor? Somehow I felt reluctant to trust her.

Mike and Jan argued with me, trying to get me to forget my personal feelings and accept Loma Linda's offer. Besides this battle wasn't about the plight of Brenda Winner and her disgust with Loma Linda University Medical Center. It was about the fate of our unborn son or daughter and bringing something good out of the loss we have all suffered. It was about saving sick babies who otherwise might die. It was about preventing the needless suffering of our baby. Most of all, talking it over with Dr. Platt finally changed my mind. After all, this was our only chance, he convinced me. I couldn't throw it away now. Finally, after a few days of waffling, I called Dr. Platt and told him to go ahead and make the arrangements for us to participate in the new protocol.

In the meantime, Jan and I stopped into Dr. Suvannee's office for a final prenatal checkup. She was delighted that Loma Linda was willing to help us, even if what they were offering wasn't quite what Mike and I had in mind. Dr. Suvannee's enthusiasm rubbed off on me. Seeing her always seemed to boost my confidence. We had a very nice visit and even had Jan listen to the baby's heartbeat with the stethoscope.

After the announcement of the protocol in early December, we were in demand for interviews more than ever. It seemed like every local TV affiliate in Southern California called us at least once to congratulate us and to get our reaction to the announcement. I then got a call from Mark and Missy Hanrahan, a young couple who live in Sparks, Nevada. Missy had given birth to an anencephalic only two weeks before the announcement of the protocol. They were very supportive, and their phone call was very personal and very touching, but the protocol came too late for them. That evening there were even more interviews. By this time even the foreign press was getting into the act. I spoke with a reporter from London by the name of Barbara Jones. She came over and spent about four hours interviewing me and taking pictures. She told the name of the doctor who was sent to prison in the UK — Magdi Yacoub. She said he transplanted a heart taken from an anencephalic donor before the brain death criteria were met. He went to prison, even though the little girl who received the heart is still alive and well. She also told me that he was out of prison now, but that he was very private and would not talk to the press.

I was getting very tired of the interview process, and I was beginning to feel like I was continually repeating myself. I was getting very big, and Mike was getting very tired from the constant bombardment of appointments, questions, and photo shoots. But we were very intent in getting our message out in as many ways to as many people as possible, so we went on doing the interviews — and neither one of us complained.

Within a few days Dr. Sherman called and went over all the necessary paperwork and bureaucratic red tape that had to be taken care of, now that they were establishing a protocol for anencephalic organ donors. Once the baby was born, she told me, it would be put on a respirator to oxygenate the organs until brain death could be determined. The ventilator would also make the death less traumatizing, which was also one of my concerns. There was something about this woman that I definitely did not like, and my reluctance must have come across to her loud and clear. She said that Dr. Sakala would be handling the delivery. I was very relieved. We were also to be at Loma Linda that coming Saturday for a meeting with the staff to discuss the plans for my delivery.

Upon our arrival, we were met with a warm and open reception. I was pleasantly surprised. This was quite a turn around from the initial reaction I got from these people. But now the spotlight of the national media was upon them, and they had to at least act like the caring benefactors of Mike and Brenda Winner, if only for the benefit of the public relations department. Mike asked the head PR spokesman for Loma Linda if we could meet Dr. Bailey.

"Dr. Bailey had his time in the spotlight," he abruptly told us. "Now it is Sherman's turn."

OK, I thought, here is someone who just a few weeks ago basically told me to give up and to quit trying to do the impossible. Now here I am — seeing to it that she has her turn in the spotlight. How am I supposed to react to that? Dr. Sherman greeted me with a clear message that read "Shut up, go have your baby, and quit bothering me." Now, with all the media attention, things have changed a bit. Now she was prepared to offer me a brave and brilliant new idea. I guess I should feel grateful, but in truth I took comfort in the fact that Dr. Sherman was not going to do the delivery.

We met Dr. Sakala, and he was very nice. Mike and I both immediately liked him. He assured us that they would take all possible steps to ensure the safest and the easiest delivery possible. They would not perform a Cesarean delivery unless it was absolutely necessary. The reason was that a Cesarean was usually only necessary to protect the life of the baby, not the life of the mother. He told me that I shouldn't have to go through one and carry a scar as long as the baby could be delivered vaginally. I could have pain medication, or if I desired, I could have none at all. It was entirely up to me.

As we walked down the hallway to Dr. Sherman's office, Mike and I spotted a familiar looking gray-haired gentleman. It was the famous Dr. Bailey. Mike stopped him in the hallway and introduced us, and although he was polite, he did not seem very anxious to chat with us. Since he might be the one who transplants our baby's organs, he didn't want to appear too friendly. Loma Linda did not want to project the appearance of recruiting organ donors. He was also very tense and sweaty, as if he had just finished some hairy operation and was due a good, strong martini. Dr. Bailey nodded goodbye and headed off quickly down the hall. Mike and I decided to leave our introduction at that.

We sat down for a long discussion with Dr. Sherman in her office about the details of the protocol and the contingent arrangements to be made if the baby was stillborn. She also went to great lengths to warn us about the evils of the press and how they would turn this whole thing against us if we weren't very, very careful. I thought it was ironic that Dr. Sherman felt the need to warn me about the press and how they might chew me up and spit me out. After all, it was only because I brought this whole issue to the attention of the media in the first place that any of this was happening. It seemed to me that she was more interested in turning down the heat in the kitchen than she was in safeguarding our tender feelings.

Everything finally looked good for the delivery. We left Loma Linda that day feeling that things in general were in pretty good shape. We liked Dr. Sakala, and I was satisfied that even if Dr. Sherman was involved, it would be only in a semi-peripheral way. The next day was a Sunday. It was overcast and very windy. Mike was called into work for emergency repairs on some downed power lines, and he had to stay continuously on his shift until 5:00 P.M. the next day. The poor guy was exhausted, but somehow we still kept pace with doing our interviews.

On that following Tuesday I came down with the worst case of cramps I had ever experienced in my life. I thought to myself "This is it!" Jan, Christi, and Mike all headed out with me to the hospital. We ended up at Santa Teresita Hospital. Dr. Suvannee was there, but we came up empty. No baby. Dr. Suvannee came in later to assure me that I was only experiencing false labor. The contraction pains had really hurt, but after a while I was feeling better. Finally we went home to bed.

71

By the next day I was feeling pretty good. Joanna Salamandra from SCOPPC came over to meet us and congratulate us on the protocol. She was a petite woman with a slender build, but very attractive. She was also a truly wonderful person. She had taught me so much, and I felt like I owed her tremendously. It meant a great deal to me that she took the time to come out and visit with us.

While Jan and I were visiting with Joanna, the phone suddenly rang. I picked it up, and I found myself on the other end of the line with a spokesperson from the Right-to-Life chapter in Palm Desert, an affluent desert community near Palm Springs. In a deceptively civilized and sympathetic voice she first told me how sorry she was about our tragedy and everything that we were going through. Then she switched to a more authoritative tone and informed that if there were any "unscrupulous events" planned, that the RTL was watching. They were "willing to go on bended knee to the ends of the Earth to make sure this baby's rights were protected." She also told me that they were going to publicly protest Loma Linda's decision to establish the protocol, assuring me that they were serious about "putting a stop to fetal abuse."

They were going to protest my delivery! I was stoked! These jerks gave me just the final jolt I needed to get pumped up all over again. I couldn't even feel the fatigue of all those trips to the hospital and doing all those interviews anymore. Joanna seemed shocked and surprised at my reaction to the Right-to-Life call. I guess she wasn't used to being around people who get as feisty as I do when I'm up against a tough opponent. I kept pacing the room, shouting "Bring 'em on!" and "I can't wait!" over and over again. Boy did I want a piece of those guys! Joanna complemented me on my determination, and she promised that she would offer all the support she could in the meantime while we tried to pull this thing off.

"Now I know what you meant," she said, "when you said 'If someone else had pushed this hard before, I wouldn't have to go through any this.'"

The next day we were scheduled to go on Nightline. It was going to be a big moment for us — our first live appearance on a news show. The ABC people had scheduled two ethicists, Art Caplan, who was more or less supportive of exploring the possibilities, and Lester Capon, who was firmly opposed to organ donations by anencephalics, to also be on the show. Mr. Capon was a law professor and was an author of the brain death law. Dr. Caplan was director of the Center for Biomedical Ethics at the University of Minnesota. They had also arranged for Greg and Gail Merell to appear. They were a couple who wanted to donate the organs of their anencephalic baby for transplantation back in 1982. I was excited about going on live TV, but then I started feeling sick. We had to cancel at the last minute.

Later we watched the program at home on our own TV, and we were very impressed with Dr. Caplan and his calm rational demeanor. So many people seemed to be screaming at us, from either one side or the other. It was nice to hear someone discuss the issues without getting all emotional about it. The other guy just seemed to justify his side by using the usual fear tactic of arguing that if we allow organs to be taken from anencephalics, then it will set a precedent to harvest organs from other types of terminal patients. If we allow this one exception to the brain death law, then no one on a respirator will be safe. Hell, those unscrupulous, organ-mongering doctors wouldn't hesitate for a moment to use this thing to build a new transplants-to-the-highest-bidder empire. Is that what people are really afraid of?

Each day the media attention got closer and closer to overwhelming me. Our phone was constantly ringing, with reporters from newspapers, radio, magazines, and TV begging us to let them be the first ones to break the news when the baby was born. Finally, I quit answering the phone and let the answering machine handle the messages.

Finally my due date came — December 16. I had no contractions, no labor pains, but the reality that I could give birth at any moment was really starting to hit me. Every day for the last week or two when Mike took off for work, I would spend long hours worrying whether he would be here when the big moment finally came. I was also thinking long and hard about what I was going to do after the baby was born, depending on the outcome of the delivery. Each of possible scenarios seemed equally chilling. If the baby was stillborn, there would be no transplant of course, but in a way that seemed the least frightening of all the possibilities to me. At least our baby wouldn't suffer, and the trauma would be over relatively quickly.

I called Dr. Sakala at Loma Linda to make the last minute plans for my delivery. I asked about the details of the protocol. He told me that if it was a live birth, the baby would be taken to intensive care and put on a respirator if it showed signs of respiratory distress. He also assured me that even if the baby was stillborn, I could still hold the baby and look at it, if I wanted to. It was totally up to me. But he did say that, while he could understand my anxieties, the worst kind of fear was fear of the unknown. Maybe by holding the baby and not being afraid to look at it, I would be able to conquer my fears and more easily accept what happened to us. Although Dr. Sakala sounded very convincing, I still wasn't sure of my feelings. I told him that I would let him know what I wanted to do.

I also made arrangements with Dr. Sakala to come into the hospital through a service elevator. I would be registered under a fictitious name. The parking lot at Loma Linda had become a field headquarters for the media covering the delivery, and a crowd of reporters had been camping out there for days in anticipation of the big moment. A horrifying scenario for our arrival at the hospital lingered in the back of my mind. It was the vision of Mike and Jan dragging me through a large crowd of people gathered out in front of the hospital. Each of them are hauling me along with one arm while busily fending off the newsmen, photographers, and curiosity seekers with the other. I'm delirious from the painkillers they've given me on the way to the hospital, but I'm still babbling random facts about anencephaly to the crowd. The cruelest part is the barrage of stupid questions thrown at me by the media as I go by.

"How do you feel about losing your baby, Mrs. Winner?" they ask.

"Thirty-five-hundred births a year are anencephalic," I reply.

"Are you happy Loma Linda established this protocol, Mrs. Winner?" they counter.

"All are doomed to die a short time after birth," I reply.

"Would you do it all again, Mrs. Winner?" The final whammy is delivered.

"No one knows what causes it," I reply.

I just couldn't face all those news hounds and experience the trauma of childbirth at the same time. That was just too much to deal with.

After talking with Dr. Sakala, my thoughts returned to whether or not I should hold the baby after it was born. I decided that Dr. Sakala was right, that I needed to look at and hold my baby, even if it was stillborn. Even though the thought of it gave me chills, I

74

knew that I had to hold my baby, no matter what he or she looked like. We had been through so much together, to not even hold the baby now amounted to the same thing as turning my back on the baby from the beginning. I didn't fight my way here to wimp out now. Besides this whole thing was about facing up to the issues and not turning away from difficult decisions. I knew I had to do it, no matter what condition the baby was in. I finally felt ready for this thing to happen.

CHAPTER IX

By December 20 I was four days past due, and I was getting a little impatient. Up to now we had hoped that the baby would come naturally, but Dr. Platt had told me early on that mothers of anencephalics don't always give birth on their own. Often labor must be induced artificially. Labor is stimulated by a hormone that is secreted by the pituitary gland in the brain of the fetus, he explained. If the pituitary gland is underdeveloped or absent, no hormone can be produced, and the mother never goes into labor. Dr. Platt told me of one woman in Arkansas who carried an anencephalic baby for fifteen months before they discovered the baby's condition. She simply believed that her baby wasn't ready to come out yet. Other times, especially when the mother is unaware of her baby's condition, the baby comes out right on schedule, only for the parents to receive the most untimely shock of their lives. Every individual case was different, and anything was possible.

By the time Mike got home from work that evening, I was beginning to feel like the time had come to go to the hospital. I wasn't having any contractions or pain, but something inside of me, something instinctual, signaled to me that now was the right time to go. Besides Christmas was right around the corner, and this thing needed to be over with — one way or another. I had Mike and Jan here with me right now, an obvious advantage that I might lose if I waited. Finally we made the big decision. Mike called into work about 8:00 P.M. to tell them we were going in for the delivery. I called Loma Linda, and they agreed to meet us at the service elevator entrance in a couple hours.

We didn't arrive until around 11:00 P.M. We got into the hospital without a hitch. A small entourage of Loma Linda people, including the public relations director and chaplain, were there at the door to greet us. They took me upstairs in a wheelchair and gave me my new name, Judith Jones, which would serve as my identity during my stay in the hospital. It was a rather ironic choice, since I knew a nurse named Judy Jones who worked at SCOPPC. The chaplain was particularly nice to me, a woman by the name of Bronwen Watts. She was very attentive and seemed genuinely concerned with my emotional and physical well being.

As I was waiting in the treatment room near the maternity ward, a pleasant-looking young nurse walked in. I was very much surprised when she came up to me, smiled, and took hold of my hand.

"I'm so glad to meet you, Mrs. Winner. I hope you know what an honor it is for us to take care of you."

"Honor?" I replied in amazement. "What makes it such an honor to take care of me?"

"Well you see, Mrs. Winner, I hold anencephalic babies in my arms all the time. Sometimes I hold them for their entire lives. It makes me sad to see them die. But it makes me even sadder to see the baby next to them die because it needed a new liver. You and Mike are trying to change that."

Mike came in the treatment room and sat down next me on the bed. I was genuinely touched by what that nurse had said to me. The whole episode was proof that I got through to at least one person out there who didn't know me four months ago. I guess there's a big difference between massaging your philosophical and ethical position for the cameras and facing the reality of what is happening down in the trenches where the babies are dying. That nurse understood our point of view because she had lived with it and seen it for herself. She didn't care about the philosophical debate, she cared about the dying babies. It was the best kind of affirmation I could hope to get.

Before they started to work on me, Mike and I signed an agreement to have any remains which were not used for organ transplantation delivered to Dr. Platt for further study after the baby's death. Then the nurse started me on an intravenous tube.

They gave me the shot to start my labor and wheeled my bed down to the maternity ward.

After about twenty minutes I felt my first contraction. It was awful, and I asked them for an anesthetic. One of Dr. Sakala's assistants gave me an epidural injection of painkiller. Soon I couldn't feel a thing. I was completely oblivious to everything that was happening from my shoulders down. I was in a peaceful euphoria, and Mike and Bronwen were right there to provide moral support if I drifted into any angst. A few hours passed by, and there was still no cervical dilation. This could be a long haul, but I didn't care. I was feeling surprisingly optimistic, cutting jokes and acting silly with the doctors. The painkillers were doing a hell of a job.

Still more hours passed, and I wasn't making any progress. I was totally relying on nature. I couldn't feel anything to push against, so the baby was on its own. Mike and Bronwen were hanging right there with me. We talked about the protocol and all the possible outcomes. Time seemed to drift on endlessly, giving me plenty of chances to sift through my old doubts. Finally after twenty hours in the delivery room, one of Dr. Sakala's assistants decided that enough was enough, and he broke my water.

Things then started to happen very quickly. I watched the pulsing panel of instruments on the twin displays next to my bed. They showed my heartbeat side by side with the baby's heartbeat. The head of the baby started to emerge. I heard someone on the medical team say that she was face up. Ordinarily they could help the baby along by pulling the head, but with an anencephalic there's nothing to pull. The baby was just kind of stuck at face-level and was having trouble emerging any farther. Dr. Sakala decided that I need a number five episiotomy, which is the most drastic of the incision patterns used to aid childbirth. It involves five cuts both vertically and laterally around the vagina. Still, the baby struggled to emerge.

My anxiety level started to surge as I watched the baby's heartbeat speed up on the electrocardiogram screen. It was as if my baby knew that its doom was lingering close by, and it was fighting with all its strength to keep from coming out to meet that doom. Finally the baby presented its shoulders. But before they could even pull her free and tell me that it was a girl, I knew she was gone. No one had to say a thing. I could feel it the very moment that she died.

I will never forget that moment, when I saw her heartbeat turn to a steady baseline on the TV monitor. It filled me with a strange mixture of anguish and relief. Our ordeal was finally over. The long hours I spent trying to understand and accept this blurry concept called "anencephaly" had instantly dissolved away into vividly stark reality. It was the moment Mike and I always dreamed about, only somehow gone terribly crazy. It was supposed to be the moment when we heard the cries of our newborn daughter for the first time. Instead we were engulfed by a chasm of silence, cast in long shadows of sadness, grief, and pain. The medical team tried to revive her, but I knew it was no use. My beautiful baby daughter was gone.

They took her away to clean her up and dress her in a diaper. For the first time since I found out that my baby was not going to live, a torrent of emotion flooded through me. I cried my eyes out uncontrollably. The gusher of pent up emotion that I first expected those four and half months ago had finally arrived, and the terrible dejection and sense of tragedy that I detached myself from then erupted through me with devastating force. It was as if when they took her from me, it was finally over. My burden was lifted, and crying suddenly became easy again. The moment that I had been dreading had finally passed, and the ordeal was over once and for all. I could let go now. Thank God that Mike was right beside me the whole way. I don't know how I could have faced that terrible moment alone.

I asked one of the doctors if I could see and hold my baby. They brought her in wrapped in a blanket and a diaper with a little cap to cover her open skull. She was still warm, and even though she had passed away, she still seemed to fit perfectly in my arms. Mike held her too. Except for the little skullcap, you could hardly tell that this wasn't just another normal, healthy, sleeping baby. It was so amazing to me that this once very lively baby could be so perfect from the eyes down and so different from the eyes up.

I took off the skullcap and the diaper and looked her over from head to toe. I know it sounds kind of morbid, but I had to look over every inch of my baby. This was my only chance to know her. I had to take off that cap and see for myself what she looked like underneath it. What was this thing, "anencephaly," that kept her from being with me. I had to confront it, even if it meant looking straight away at something hideous.

Finally I gathered enough strength to look into her head. Everything was missing: the bone, the tissue, the skin. All I could see was the brain stem at the base of her neck. I stared down into Jarren's head for just a minute or two, but it felt like an eternity. I thought I was prepared for the moment, but it was terribly shocking to see that horrible sight right there before me, the sight of the emptiness that had claimed so much happiness. I felt like I should cry, but I couldn't muster a tear. Coming face to face with the reality of our tragedy seemed too unreal, too appalling for me to bear right now.

They took the baby from me and wheeled me into the recovery room. Mike and his dad were waiting for me there. Dr. Sherman told me that they only let the Associated Press reporters into the hospital, but that they would release the news of the delivery to the other news agencies. They brought us the release papers to sign so that the organs could be used legally for transplantation. Unfortunately, since the baby was stillborn, the organs were not of any use. Still, we signed the release anyway. I asked them if I could have one last look at my baby before they took her away for good. By this time the baby was cold and blue, but still I could have held her and looked at her forever. Mike chided me that I was being morbid, so I finally gave in and told them to take her away.

One of the nurses brought us a form to sign. It was an authorization to donate the remains for scientific study. This was an option we had discussed with Dr. Platt, and we decided that we wanted the remains to be made available to him.

Mike held my hand by the bedside as we talked about our ordeal and the short life of our daughter. We decided to name her Jarren. Mike and I had decided between two names for the baby early in my pregnancy. If it was a boy, we were going to name our baby Rusty, after Mike's younger brother who was killed as a teenager in a golf cart accident. If it was a girl, we were going to name her Brandy. I started to have a change of heart later on about naming a little girl Brandy, and I saw the name Jarren on a movie credit one night on TV. Mike insisted on Brandy, but once we found out the baby wasn't going to live, I decided I was going to name this baby anything I wanted to. So, boy or girl, our baby's name was going to be Jarren.

The next day was two days before Christmas. I wasn't in much of a holiday mood, and the shock and trauma of the last two days had left me emotionally drained. I was intent on spending the day just lying in my hospital bed and quietly recuperating with Mike by my side. Suddenly, an unfamiliar doctor appeared in my hospital room. He walked over and greeted me, and grabbed the medical chart from the end of my bed. I looked at the nametag and instantly recognized the name; it was none other than Dr. Norman Brothers. This was one of the doctors who told me to "give up" back when I first called Loma Linda about organ donation.

"I understand that congratulations are in order!" Dr. Brothers opened without first looking at my chart.

I was in total shock. What did he mean "congratulations"? Was this some kind of sick joke? Suddenly Dr. Brothers recognized who I was from reading my medical chart. Obviously he wasn't aware that I had just given birth to an anencephalic infant — until that moment. He turned bright red, and then bolted abruptly out the room. He didn't offer any apology or acknowledgment of his mistake. He just ran for the hills.

Dr. Brothers' visit sent my spirits into a tailspin. Was it a painful little accident, or was everybody around here really that disconnected? Maybe the others were just a little better at covering it up. Right when I was sinking to a particularly low ebb, a little nine-year-old boy named John Hernandez came into my room and handed me a get well card. He was a patient in the hospital too. He was awaiting a kidney transplant. Nine years old and he's having a kidney transplant. And they said I was brave. Anyway it was a real sweet hand-drawn sympathy card with the words "I'm sorry your baby died." written in crayon on the inside. It was so sincere. What a wonderful kid. If only Dr. Brothers had grown up that sensitive.

The next day was Christmas Eve. Mike and I had a meeting that morning with Dr. Sherman and Gus Cheatum, head of the Loma Linda Hospital public relations department. They wanted to release a press statement, and they needed our authorization to do so. I insisted that Mike and I write the statement to be released. Although at first they were reluctant, both Dr. Sherman and the PR guy approved of it once they read our statement. It was now time to face the news hounds.

Mike and I were escorted to the waiting room being used by the press. The cameras and flashbulbs that once laid anxiously in waiting for us had all made their way back home. Only a single TV camera crew — the local Los Angeles affiliate of CBS — was there waiting for us. Mike read our statement while I sat back in a wheelchair and looked on.

"First of all, we wish to thank Loma Linda University Medical Center for their decision in setting the protocol and for their concern and compassion during this emotionally difficult time.

"Jarren was very important to us and eventually the whole world. Unfortunately, she did not make it far enough to utilize the protocol. But she was able to open the door for future anencephalic angels to live on.

"Brenda and I still have strong convictions concerning anencephaly, and we will continue to seek answers to all the questions that arise.

"To all of the people in the world that supported us and have been so kind, we thank you. To everyone that has been in a similar situation, we are with you. To the press and media, we thank you for presenting us in a most proper perspective."

The press conference was sort of a let down after all the attention we attracted before the baby was born, but I was glad to have the ordeal over with and be able to get home. The thought of sleeping in my own bed was very appealing right now, and I was anxious to get on with the business of our lives. We left the hospital right after the press conference was over.

When we walked in the front door, I was stunned to find Jan totally obscured by flowers. There must have been fifty different arrangements crammed into our tiny two-bedroom apartment. I was actually flattered that so many people sent us flowers, but this was ridiculous. I started a free flower give away. The neighbors, friends, passers by, I hit on all of them. Finally I was able to gain us some breathing room.

Jan relayed several messages that had come in on the answering machine while I was in the hospital. First the reporter from Time magazine called. He didn't say much except that "the story died along with the baby." Kind of a cold, calculating bunch, these reporters. Another message was from the ABC Nightline reporter who was assigned to our story, a man named George Strait. He was more personal, offering his condolences, but added, "once you're news, you're old news fast" to his message.

Clearly, I had left the masses disappointed with my performance. The stakes were set, the betting lines were drawn, and everyone who bet on the successful transplant scenario lost their shirt. I had achieved a major downer. Now the audience was walking out, holding back their applause, and grumbling quietly to themselves as they filed away to the parking lot.

My friends Paula and Eric came by and cheered me up by giving me a special present. I guess there's an astronomical society somewhere that for a small fee will allow you to "buy" a star and have it named after you or someone you designate. I thought it was kind of a neat gift, but it didn't have what you would call equity value. Still I was very touched that they had thought of me and bought me such a personal and thoughtful gift.

Finally Christmas Day arrived. I relished in the peace and quiet that only Christmas Day can bring. No phone calls. No pressure from the media or religious zealots. Just an easygoing, uneventful Christmas Day.

Jan left for New Mexico the following morning. I couldn't find the words to tell her how much I appreciated having her there to help me. For the last month or two I had been totally preoccupied with this organ donation thing while Jan basically ran the rest of my life. To have someone like that behind you is a feeling of satisfaction and strength that can get you through almost any crisis. We hugged and said our good-byes, and then she was on her way back home.

A few days later both my mom and sister, Deeanne, flew out from New Mexico to visit and offer moral support. After seeing my mom, I completely fell apart emotionally. Something about seeing her made it easy to cry. It was like I was a kid again. Now that Mom was here, she could make it all better. The three of us stayed up very late talking about the baby and the ordeal Mike and I had just been through.

The next day was New Year's Eve. We had scheduled a memorial service for Jarren for that evening. The chaplain from LLUMC, Bronwen Watts, was going to conduct the services. A reporter for the CBS news show "On the Road with Charles Kuralt" was coming by to do an interview. Right before they came, the phone rang unexpectedly. I picked it up to answer to a woman with a formal and unfamiliar voice.

"Mrs. Winner, this is Glasser-Miller-Lamb Mortuary in Arcadia. We need authorization to proceed with the cremation that Loma Linda Hospital has requested."

"What?" I answered with surprise. "The remains were supposed to be delivered to Dr. Platt at USC County Medical Center."

"No, Mrs. Winner, we have your baby here. You just need to come in and sign the authorization papers."

I was incensed. That Sherman person was obviously talking out the other side of her mouth when she said she would see to it that the remains were delivered to Dr. Platt. I thought that was going to happen no matter what the outcome of the delivery.

The woman from the mortuary said that even though tomorrow was New Year's Day, she would open up the place especially for me so that the matter could be taken care of.

I immediately called Dr. Platt. He told me that he thought it was strange that the remains never arrived, but he was hesitant to call us. He thought that maybe we had changed our minds. He also told me that he couldn't reach anyone at Loma Linda either. Nobody would return his calls. The whole episode made me want to wring a certain doctor's neck. I can't stand it when people bullshit me. It was becoming obvious to me that she had plenty of sincerity when it came to crafting an image of herself as a great humanitarian or the next great organ transplant pioneer. That is, she's sincere when the press is watching. After all, they saw her as the striding professional, trying to bring medical ethics and clinical practice together in the most humane way possible.

That all sounded really good in print, but in reality I think she saw our situation as more a liability than an opportunity. It was like we had the words "bad press" written all over us. Although in public the protocol was her proud creation, I definitely got the feeling that Dr. Sherman really saw the entire situation as a very hot and very sticky predicament. It was obvious to me that the sooner the whole issue was disposed of, the better off she would feel.

By the time the reporter and photographer arrived for our interview, I was positively livid, and I'm afraid I didn't make the best impression as the grieving mother. I was so upset I hardly said anything, and the interview attempt rapidly spiraled into nowhere. I couldn't get this whole mortuary thing out of my head. Why did Sherman do that to me?

The interview went so badly that they didn't even use us in their report. Bronwen Watts, the chaplain at LLUMC, conducted a memorial service for Jarren that evening. We held the service in our apartment for family and close friends.

Bronwen immediately took notice of my sullen mood and asked me what was bothering me. I told her about the mortuary episode, and how Dr. Sherman refused to return my calls. She immediately called Dr. Sherman. Obviously she knew the phone number where you could get an answer. Bronwen stepped off into the bedroom where I couldn't overhear their conversation.

A few minutes later, Bronwen came out of the bedroom with the phone in her hands.

"Brenda, Dr. Sherman says that they looked at the organs. Everything was fine, and they put them back."

"What?" I contested indignantly. "We wanted the organs to be donated for research. Dr. Platt has been waiting for them for a week!"

Bronwen relayed my response to Dr. Sherman over the phone. It was a good thing Bronwen was there to mediate, because I kept trying to grab away the phone. I wanted to give Sherman the up close and personal treatment, the kind of tongue-lashing I was famous for. Bronwen listened to Dr. Sherman's response, and then calmly repeated it back to me.

"Dr. Sherman says," Bronwen said, "that she thought it was in your best interest to send the baby to a mortuary to be cremated. The media might blow this thing out of proportion and make the public think you're being cruel by donating the baby to science."

"Well, why did we sign the consent forms? We checked off everything we wanted to donate. That is what we feel is in our best interest."

I impatiently waited for Dr. Sherman's next response.

"Now remember, Brenda," Bronwen relayed, "you had an epidural injection. You were drugged all day. There are no consent forms. Dr. Sherman doesn't think you signed any. Are you sure you signed something the day of the delivery?"

"Hey this is bullshit," Mike interrupted. "I was there. I wasn't on drugs. I signed them. I watched her sign them."

"I was there too!" Mike's dad broke in. "I signed the papers as a witness, and I damn sure wasn't on drugs!"

Bronwen stepped back into the bedroom to finish off her conversation with Dr. Sherman. A few minutes later she came out with the phone back on the hook.

"Everything's all right now, Brenda," she tried to reassure me. "I'll find out what happened. There's got to be an answer. If there's a problem, Dr. Sherman said the cremation has already been paid for. But in the meantime might I suggest we get on with the services? I mean, we should do it for Jarren's sake."

I reluctantly agreed, but Dr. Sherman's feeble, secondhand excuses left me unsatisfied. Obviously something had gone wrong, and she wasn't about to admit what it was. It must have something to do with me having an alias while I was in the hospital. The paperwork must have gotten screwed up, with Brenda Winner's baby scheduled to be sent to the mortuary, and Judy Jones' baby getting donated to science. The only problem was that Judy Jones didn't have a baby.

I was also incensed that Dr. Sherman thought I was upset about spending money on Jarren's cremation. I can just see her sitting at home thinking to herself "It's already paid for, so what is she complaining about?" How I wished we could pay for the cremation ourselves. I hated being a charity case.

After a while I settled down, especially when the services began. It was a nice ceremony, and Bronwen read a poem for us all that she had written for Jarren. Afterward, a friend of ours who is a minister, Terry Keenan, also gave a eulogy service. Although I appreciated the sentiment on everyone's part, I couldn't concentrate on the services. I was still fuming about how the mortuary thing was handled and the way Dr. Sherman refused to deal with me directly. Did she think I was that stupid, to believe that I was too drugged to remember signing papers that I knew I damn well signed?

The next day I went down to the mortuary to sign the release papers to have the baby cremated. The more I thought about it, the angrier I became at Dr. Sherman. I tried to call her, but of course she was always out of her office. She never returned my calls.

CHAPTER X

The next few days after New Year's Day were quiet and uneventful. Dr. Sherman was still not returning my phone calls. Mom, Deeanne, and I spent a few quality days together shopping and hanging out. On the day that Mom and Deeanne were supposed to leave, January 4th, I received a phone call from a TV station in Cincinnati requesting an on-the-spot interview. I instantly agreed, of course, and the host of the show — a gentleman by the name of Ira Fisher — was very kind and sympathetic. It was especially exciting because Mike's mom, who lives in Cincinnati, was also on the show. She was connected up live with us on the air via a telephone link with the radio station.

I felt somewhat reassured. It was nice to know that the world had not completely lost interest in our story. Later that day Mom and Deeanne took off for home in New Mexico. I was back to being on my own again. Things were nowhere near as hectic as before the baby was born, but somehow I knew this anencephalic organ donor thing was not going to just curl up and go away. The news media may have had its field day with it, but as usual, they've left very little resolved. They'll be back. Just as long as people keep having babies, this thing is going to crop up over and over again. Hopefully something like the protocol will be there for them, and they won't have to fight for it like Mike and I had to. But even the protocol, which was the closest thing to a real accomplishment that Mike and I had to show for all our efforts, left me with some very disturbing unanswered questions.

Apparently I was not alone. It was only a few weeks after the baby's birth when I read in the paper about a bill being introduced in Sacramento by a state assemblyman from Inglewood. The bill, authored by a gentleman named Curtis Tucker, called for an immediate moratorium on the LLUMC protocol. The article said he would introduce the bill when the state legislature came into session later in January. The newspaper article quoted him as saying that he was "appalled" by the protocol and its approach of keeping anencephalic babies on life support until they could be used as organ donors.

In response, I began a massive letter writing campaign. I wrote my state assemblyman and my state senator. I even wrote a letter to the governor. Any time I got hold of the name of a new politician or bureaucrat, I sent them a letter stating my viewpoint and asking them for their position in return. I always included a copy of the protocol with letters. Although I still believed in the political system, I did wonder if my letters were going to get any response from Sacramento.

The next few days were quiet, except for an interview with USA Today on the aftermath of our experience. The reporter's name was Sally Stuart. She was very pleasant and nice, but the same high-pitched excitement as before the baby was born was obviously missing from the story. I felt uninspired and burnt out by the whole business. After you've repeated something over and over, it gets harder and harder to convince yourself that it's still fresh. I don't want to be boring people by rehashing a familiar story. Still, with a bill to stop the protocol about to be introduced into the state legislature, I felt like I couldn't give up.

A couple of days later I received a phone call from Bronwen Watts, the chaplain from Loma Linda. She mentioned that the Ethics Committee of the American Medical Association was having meeting at LLUMC, and the protocol and the ethics of using anencephalics as organ donors were going to be major topics of discussion. She invited Mike and me to attend the conference as guests of LLUMC. The meeting was scheduled for January 13. I told her that although Mike could not take off work to be there, I would be glad to attend. I assured her that I wanted to help anyway I could.

I felt a little better now. At least they hadn't completely forgotten about me back at Loma Linda. After shutting me out completely for the last couple weeks, they finally opened the door again — if only by a little crack. I guess I should take advantage of the opportunity. Besides, even though the protocol didn't make use of Jarren's organs, it was still going strong enough that it might be successful with another donor infant. I resolved that I had an obligation to offer whatever support I could muster for the protocol, if only for the sake of the sick babies out there that might be saved.

The next day yielded even more signs that there was still a lot of interest in the follow-up to our story. I did a live interview over the phone with a PBS radio station in San Diego. I received a call from the producer of a local morning TV show in Seattle, a woman by the name of Dana Newton. Her show was called "Good Company", and they were interested in flying us up to Seattle to do a taped interview. They wanted us to leave Sunday, January the 17th, and do the taping the following Monday morning. Mike agreed that he would go with me for the taping.

On the day before the AMA Ethics Committee Meeting at LLUMC, January 12th, I got another call for an interview. This time it was Mary Kay Clinton, producer of the Oprah Winfrey Show. They were planning a show on anencephalic organ donors and asked me if Mike and I would be interested in being two of the panel members. I was pretty excited. This wasn't some local-yokel lightweight talk show calling. This was Oprah Winfrey. This was the big time. This was a chance to "wow" the public. Unfortunately, the timing was all wrong for Mike. There was no way he could make both the Seattle trip and also do the Oprah interview. I wasn't very enthusiastic about facing the cameras without Mike by my side, but I decided to accept their offer to appear anyway.

The meeting at LLUMC was scheduled to start at noon the next day. I arrived a little early. Everyone was very cordial and very nice to me, but I felt somewhat out of place among all the hot shot doctors and political mucky-mucks who were in attendance. The news media were also there in full force, and they seemed to pay a lot of attention to me, asking me how we were doing and so forth, although I wasn't sure how much of it was sincere. I sat through a number of long-winded speeches, not understanding very much of the medical details. One fact that was abundantly clear to me though was that everyone had a different opinion on the subject. Nobody seemed quite sure what to do about anencephalic organ donors. And nobody was asking me.

Finally, Dr. Bailey gave a short talk and set the stage for the keynote speaker, Dr. Sherman. All in all, Dr. Sherman's speech went well. Boredom is a great controversy killer, and for the time being no one in the crowd was calling out for her head on a skewer. They introduced me to the audience, and I stood up for a polite round of applause. You would think from the way Dr. Sherman described me to the audience that we were old sorority buddies. I was careful to avoid mentioning to anyone that this was the first I had heard or seen from her since the baby's delivery.

After the meeting, Dr. Sherman asked me if she could talk to me privately in her office. We went in with Dr. Bailey and Gus Cheatum, the Loma Linda PR guy, joining us in tow. Dr. Sherman closed the door.

"Did you ever find those papers we signed to have Jarren's organs delivered to Dr. Platt at USC?" I opened. I hoped that now that we were face to face, Dr. Sherman would finally give me the real story about what happened concerning Jarren's remains.

"No, we never found them," Dr. Sherman answered. "Oprah Winfrey has called us," she said, quickly brushing the whole issue aside. "Has she been in touch with you?"

"Yes," I answered, "I've talked on the phone with her producer about an appearance."

"Have you decided whether to go or not?" she asked.

"Yes, I'm going to do it."

"Is Mike going with you?" she continued.

"No. He has to stay here and work. If I go, I'll be going alone."

"Well, Oprah has also invited me to appear on the show as well," said Dr. Sherman. "I'll be right there with you, in case anyone asks you a question you're uncomfortable with. Don't worry about a thing. I'll handle everything."

"OK, fine," was my simple answer.

"I'm curious who else is on the panel," said Dr. Sherman. "If it's Capon, I already know his arguments. Have you thought about what you are going to say, Brenda?"

"Well I was planning to mention that Mike and I originally wanted the organs removed at birth instead of using the protocol," I answered. "We went along with it because we felt it was the only choice open to us."

"Now Brenda, you have to understand something," answered Dr. Sherman. "Society is never going to accept harvesting organs from live babies. That's just never going to happen." Her voice took on a subdued, yet stern, quality as she continued. "The protocol is the only way that society will accept organ transplants involving anencephalic donors. You have to accept that. Just remember that we have to be careful to present the protocol as the most humane approach possible. OK?"

Dr. Bailey patted me on the shoulder with gentle reassurance. "The protocol's good," he said, almost muttering beneath his breath, "It'll work."

"We'll get together about the schedule for the taping and everything else...," Dr. Sherman finished.

Well that was that. Dr. Sherman made it clear that the only choice I had was to back the protocol. That is, unless I wanted to be one who caused the whole thing to unravel. The alternative, I guess, meant to be shut out of the process altogether. I had to forget my personal feelings. If Loma Linda wants me to be the head cheerleader for both the protocol and its originators, well then I better hang on tight and do just that. The protocol might not be perfect, but without it Mike and I clearly had nothing. I had to force myself to believe, even against my better judgment, that Dr. Sherman's way was the only way. The protocol was the only humane approach to the problem — period.

"Could I have some copies of the protocol to take with me and distribute?" I asked her timidly.

"Of course...," she answered. "Brenda, there's something else I want to talk you about. You should be very cautious about what you say or how you act in front of the media. You don't know these people like I do. They'll do anything to twist around what you say and turn it against you."

After a few more minutes of stern lecturing about the evils of the press and the TV media, we all walked out of Dr. Sherman's office. The whole experience had even further intensified my dislike for Dr. Sherman, but I decided to continue to put those feelings aside. The protocol was the most important thing now. Bronwen stopped me in the hallway, and we made our way to a secluded corner.

"Brenda, I have a proposition for you," she said to me quietly.

"Yes?"

"Would you consider coming to the next meeting of the grief counseling workshop we offer here at the hospital?"

I was a little confused. "Well, Mike and I feel that we can better deal with our grief on our own. We're really not interested in grief counseling."

"No, you don't understand," countered Bronwen. "We want you to come talk to the participants, not participate yourselves. I think you and Mike have handled your grief extremely well, and we would like to share your experiences with the group."

Although I wasn't sure what it was they wanted me to contribute, I agreed to go ahead and attend the grief counseling sessions anyway. Bronwen indicated that she would be in touch about the dates and times.

For the next few days we had visitors come in from out of town. Robin and Heather inspired an all night party at our place, but fortunately we had the whole next day to recover before we left for our TV taping in Seattle. We were scheduled to tape Good Company on the following Monday morning. Later on Paula and Eric gave us a ride to the Pasadena Hilton, where we caught a shuttle bus to the airport.

We arrived in Seattle about 12:55 Sunday night. I was extremely nervous. This was our first appearance since the birth, and I think both of our nerves were wearing thin. We seemed to fight about every little thing along the way, and our sudden apparent lack of compatibility worried me. The weather was very cold and crisp, but our hotel room was wonderful. We were on the 26th floor of the Stouffer Madison. We had a relatively good night's sleep, considering the circumstances. I called Dana Newton, the producer of the show, first thing when we woke up the next morning. It was a beautiful day outside. We set a time of 10:00 A.M. to begin the taping.

Before the interview began, I met one of the other guests scheduled to appear with us on the show. Her name was Mary Jo Kahler, and she was Executive Director for Human Life, Washington. Mike and I introduced ourselves, and I tried to be nice even though I had my problems with the Right-to-Life types. We talked briefly before the show.

"I'm glad I finally got to meet you in person," she said as we left for the sound stage. "You're so much nicer than what I've read about you in the papers."

I quietly fumed. This lady and I were off to a great start. But I couldn't afford to lose control yet. I tried to forget about our encounter.

The interview started out surprisingly well. We were on very intimate and personal terms with the hosts of the show, one male and one female, on a small sound stage. There was no audience and only a small crew, but I still felt nervous and pressured. With the Right-to-Lifer safely pushed off into the wings, I relaxed and started to feel candid and open. I was going to enjoy our moment of attention, even if the situation was only temporary. At least I would have my say first. The stage manager counted down. Three, two, one, and.... The show was underway.

"We're talking to Brenda and Michael Winner," the male co-host began, "whose daughter, Jarren, was born with a condition known as anencephaly, a birth defect where an infant is born with part or all of its brain missing. The Winners were the first participants in a new and controversial medical protocol, introduced by Loma Linda University Medical Center, to utilize anencephalic infants as badly needed organ donors. Mike and Brenda, welcome to Good Company."

The co-host turned from the camera to look at Mike and me. "What was it you felt when you first found out about Jarren?" he asked me.

I gave them my stock answer about how at first I wondered what it was I could have done to cause this terrible thing to happen. I told them about the research I did on my own and how I found out that nobody really knows what causes anencephaly. I told them how I found out that these babies were unique. They have no top part to their head, and although they have a brain stem and they will continue to grow normally in the womb, once outside the womb they cannot survive. I explained that once we found out that the organs were normal and healthy and could be used, we both immediately decided to carry the baby to full term and donate the organs.

"First of all, how did you find out?" Another familiar question.

I told him that we found out from the results of an ultrasound exam. The co-host quizzed me about the details about how we found out and what "transpired" in the ultrasound room. I told them about our experience with the nun and the doctors at Santa Teresita hospital. I told them the whole story of the ten perfect fingers and how we didn't notice at the time that the baby was anencephalic, but how we found out later from our doctor.

"Michael, when you were first told with Brenda, what went through your mind?" asked the female co-host of the show, a woman whose name I can only remember as Susan.

"A great deal of shock, of course," Mike replied. "Like Brenda said, we both went through a time when we wondered what was it that we did to create this, or whether it was because of hereditary reasons. What our doctor, Dr. Suvannee, told us when we went in was that Jarren 'was incompatible with life.' Well what does 'incompatible with life' mean? I knew right away it meant that the baby would not survive. She told us what anencephaly was and showed us some pictures in her medical books. It's not a very pretty sight, of course. All we could do then was comfort one other."

"What do they tell you?" Susan asked. "What does the medical staff, your doctor, tell you? What do friends tell you...to do? Is abortion at all raised, as it is in many cases?"

"Oh yes," I broke in, "that was the option I had. I could abort at almost six months, and that would have been OK. Or else I could carry full term. I think the doctors at first were afraid of my emotional reaction, so they wouldn't tell me anything. Now they tell me everything I want to know."

"Since this was a Catholic hospital," the male co-host interjected, "did they address the option of abortion at all?"

"Oh yes...," Mike and I answered simultaneously.

"They brought it up?" he said with some surprise. "OK. Now the question of why that wasn't an option that you seriously considered...."

"Well at almost six months, I didn't want to do that." I answered. "I could feel her moving all the time. It's kind of like I wanted proof for myself. It's not that I don't believe in abortion. I don't know, I guess that maybe I do. I'm not sure. I've never been faced with that. But at six months I just couldn't do it."

"You wanted proof," the co-host continued. "Tell us about this. You wanted proof. Proof of what?"

"Well, we could hear her heartbeat. She was moving around all the time."

"You could see her hands moving in the ultrasound," Susan added.

"Right, I could see her hands. I just wanted to see for myself. I thought maybe a mistake had been made."

I went on to tell them about the AFP test and how I refused it, thinking that everything was OK with my pregnancy. After an abbreviated version of my standard AFP lecture, they start to quiz me on our motives. Obviously they were very interested in finding out why we got involved with this thing.

"What gave you the idea then to carry your daughter full term," Susan asked next, "and to, really it seems so cold to say 'harvest its organs,' but that's basically what the idea is?"

"Yeah," I replied, "well, the decision to carry to full term, we made that immediately. We ruled out abortion. As far as donating, we didn't really know that much about the procedures. Then I saw the babies at Children's Hospital that needed livers and their parents."

"How did those parents affect you?" Susan asked.

"Oh, it tore me apart," I responded. "People say 'You and Mike are so brave.' But those people that I saw, those are brave people. They really suffer."

"You must have thought, after seeing these parents, that it would be a fairly simple proposition to...," continued the co-host.

"I thought they would be excited to hear from me," I interrupted.

"Yes, my goodness," he finished, "here's a woman who is going to do these parents such a wonderful favor."

"Well there's three hundred to five hundred babies that die a day who need livers and hearts all across the United States," I responded. I had made a gaff, but now it was too late. It's three hundred to five hundred babies a year, not a day, that die from a lack of transplantable organs. Nobody questioned it, so I went on anyway. "It just didn't make any sense. If it was OK to abort, why wasn't it OK to do this?"

"The first time you proposed this action with Jarren, what you wanted to do. Who was it to, and what kind of reaction did you get?"

The question brought a cagey smile to my face. "It was to Loma Linda University. I called there thinking that everything was going to be OK, just that the timing was crucial. So I called and asked them if I could go out there to deliver, and give them the baby. They said that was fine, but it was against the law. The baby was not considered to be brain dead. Although she was brain absent, she wasn't brain dead."

"But the child would be expected to die quite soon after birth," Susan asked. "Why can't the organs be removed and used then?"

"Because the babies still have a brain stem that controls reflexes. When they're born, and 60 percent of them are stillborn by the way, but if they are alive when they are born, they will be moving. The tear ducts, from reflexes only, will cause them to cry. But they don't make any sounds. They are totally unaware of everything around them. They feel no pain. The pain center of the brain is gone. And pain as we know it, has to go through the top part of the brain before it can affect the brain stem."

"And if the baby dies, then the process of removing the organs for donation after they have died," said the co-host, "is a futile one?"

"Yes," I answered.

"OK, we want to take a break and come back and find out more," continued the co-host. "Now struggling with a child who is anencephalic to begin with is a battle, but the battle that you undertake at this stage becomes an even more complex one, involving ethics and legalities and hospitals who turn a deaf ear to what you're trying to do, which is to really give some people and their babies a new lease on life. We'll come back with Michael and Brenda Winner on Good Company, right after this...."

I felt pretty good about how the interview was going so far. These people acted warm and sympathetic to our situation, at least so far, and it was obvious that we were going to at least get a fair hearing. We broke only briefly since the engineers fast-forwarded the tape ahead, leaving until later to edit in the commercials.

"We're talking to Michael and Brenda Winner whose daughter Jarren was born anencephalic," opened the co-host in an almost seamless carry-over to the next interview segment. "Your efforts now are to see that Jarren's life is one that is not without some purpose, even though she really isn't expected to live very long. Let's talk about what your plans were while you were still pregnant. What kinds of brick walls did you run up against?"

"The hospitals everywhere refused to even attempt to help us because of the brain death criteria surrounding it," I answered.

"Now tell us a little more about that. What exactly does that mean?" he asked me.

"Brain death is the complete and irreversible cessation of brain function, including the brain stem. The brain stem controls reflexes. They test for brain death by testing the reflexes. Since all

Jarren has is a brain stem, she will have reflexes. So until that deteriorates, she will not be considered brain dead, and by that time the organs atrophy. We didn't want them to wait that long. At the hospitals I talked to, the doctors were very afraid of it because they can be brought up on murder charges. There is a doctor in England who is up on murder charges for removing the heart of an anencephalic baby to save another baby's life."

"You found there were two instances in Canada where this had been done, didn't you?" he asked.

"Yes...with Baby Gabrielle and Baby Paul. He's the youngest heart transplant patient ever. This was done just last October. The donor was anencephalic. But the doctors were right on top of both pregnancies. When Gabrielle was born, they constantly monitored her to find out when she was going to reach brain death, When the brain stem started to deteriorate, they put her on a ventilator to oxygenate the blood. Then they delivered Paul, and Gabrielle died while on the ventilator. So when they say they are keeping the baby alive on a respirator, it's not really keeping the baby alive, since they will die on the respirators anyway. They just keep the blood oxygenated so the organs don't atrophy."

"Apart from the ethical issues raised," Susan said, "there was also a cost factor too, because it's very costly to keep a child on life support. What did your insurance agency do?"

"I called Loma Linda and asked if we could call it even," I answered with a chuckle, "thinking that it was OK. That when I found out it was against the law."

"'Call it even.' What do you mean? What did you propose to that?" responded Susan.

"I was willing to go out there and delivery the baby and just walk away...."

"You would allow the organs to be utilized from Jarren...," continued Susan, "because your insurance company pulled out?"

"Well, they would not cover me out there, since they don't cover specialties. If I could deliver at Santa Teresita, then they would cover the costs."

"So they would not cover the extraordinary extra expense of maintaining the life of the child for the purpose of using the organs," added the male co-host.

"Yes," Mike and I answered together.

"So let's place this in proximity here," he went on. "Loma Linda is not far away from where you live?"

"It's about an hour drive," Mike answered.

"What kind of research did you do with various other hospitals?" the co-host probed on. "How many hospitals did you call? What kind of reactions did you get?"

"I called hospitals all over the United States," I replied. "They all basically said the same thing. They all agreed with me. Yes, the baby's organs were normal and healthy. Yes, they could be used for transplants. But they had to wait for brain death to occur. And until then, there was no hospital willing to attempt to try, to just try. Nobody had ever heard of anencephaly, and we couldn't figure out why nobody ever talked about it. We weren't ashamed, and I wasn't just going to have the baby and put it behind me and forget about it and get on with my life."

"Did they question your character?" he asked me. "Let me ask you whether or not they felt 'here was a woman who might be a little off'?"

"Oh, they thought I was insane. Here's a woman six months pregnant, and I was screaming 'Help us!'"

"Did they allude to the fact that you were after publicity, or you were after money, or what?"

"No, no...," I replied, "they all told us basically there was an organization called the Right-to-Life that would stand in our way. Our reaction was 'Why do we have to tell them?' It's our business. It's our baby. I think that the doctors felt sorry for me, and they were very compassionate, but that's the law. There was nothing they could do about it."

"OK, you were in your ninth month," said Susan, moving the conversation forward, "and you still wouldn't give up. Then you heard from Loma Linda. What did they tell you?"

"They had decided to set a precedent, and utilize a protocol using 'modified medical management.' They would put the baby on a ventilator for one week. They would monitor the baby in that week's time twice a day by taking her off the ventilator. If she's stopped breathing on her own, then she would be determined brain dead."

"How soon was this before you gave birth?" she asked.

"About two weeks...."

"So not only were you going through the physical turmoil of carrying this child down the very last week, the very last day, but also with the emotional turmoil. Apparently now you have to deal with some publicity? What was this like for you?"

"The fight was therapeutic I think." I told her. "I wasn't emotionally upset about it. I felt very strong."

"What was the attachment to your baby like?"

"There was quite an attachment. At first I didn't want to put the baby on a ventilator. I wanted them to remove the organs immediately and have that be the cause of death. I really don't believe it when they say that she still has sucking and gagging reflexes. To me she's choking."

"There's a little difficulty here in understanding the sequence of events," said the male co-host. "Loma Linda decides to write up a protocol that is different than any other protocol than has ever been associated with anencephalics at this time."

"Right," I replied.

"When they did that, the publicity that Susan talks about, someone heard about that? Someone heard about a mother who was carrying an anencephalic child who has decided at that point to make the organs available? All of sudden the press gets a hold of that?"

"No," I answered, "what happened was there was an article in the paper about Dr. Leonard Bailey at Loma Linda, who is a heart transplant doctor. He made a comment in the paper that he could see using anencephalic children as organ donors, but he would not remove the organs from a wiggling, crying, moving baby. He said that they were thinking about putting the baby on a ventilator, but they didn't know how long to keep the baby on life support. I called the newspaper and said that I was carrying an anencephalic baby, and I didn't think they needed to put the baby on the ventilator at all."

"So you made the phone call?"

"Yes, I made the phone call."

"One other issue about the medical technology here. The reason for putting the child on the ventilator is to ensure that the physicians will have an opportunity to remove the organs before they have deteriorated?"

"It just ensures that blood will be kept pumping through the organs at all times, even when brain death occurs."

"Oh, I see," the co-host continued, "the ventilator allows the brain to die, so then they are not culpable legally for committing murder."

"You meet the brain death criteria," Mike interjected, "then you can continue with removal of those organs for donation."

99

"What happened on December 22nd, then?" Susan asked next.

"Well, when Jarren was born, she was born face up. With a normal baby they can turn the head. Since there was no skull, they had to wait for her shoulders to present, and in that time period that's when she died. There was too much pressure on the brain stem."

"So there was an inability at any time after that birth to keep her on the ventilator anyway, even after this very long fight?"

"Right," I said.

"What was usable for donation purposes for other children?"

"The corneas of the eyes and the heart valves," I answered. "In the beginning they told me that was all that they could use. I knew that they were wrong. I knew that everything else was OK. All the doctors agreed with me, yes they are OK, but they told me that they just couldn't do that."

"Are Jarren's corneas and heart valves in some other child?" the male co-host asked.

"We have no idea of knowing that," Mike answered, "and I doubt that we ever will. The organ procurement centers take care of that, and if there ever was any contact, it would be through a mediator anyway."

So ended the second segment of the taping. I was very happy with the way things were going. I was glad that Mike fielded the last question, since I didn't want to mention that we most certainly knew that Jarren's corneas and heart valves were not used in a transplant. Dr. Sherman had seen to that when she had Jarren's remains cremated. But I was glad I let it go, because it would serve no purpose at this point to dredge up such an unpleasant event of the past.

Another gentleman came onto the stage with us during the commercial break to join in the discussion. His name was Albin Teufel, and he was there to talk about his son, Alexander, who was born with biliary atresia. The start of his story was all too familiar and vividly reminded of the woman I met in the grocery store the day after Jarren was diagnosed as anencephalic. Alexander's father went on to describe their ordeal. Alexander had been through not one, but two, liver transplants.

Alexander suffered from a birth defect where the bile duct, which connects the liver with the small intestines, fails to develop. The doctors were able to temporarily prolong his life by a surgical procedure, called a casai, where part of the small intestine is

100

removed and used to fashion a makeshift bile duct. The bile duct, however, has a natural one-way valve system that prevents foreign material from traveling upstream and infecting the liver. The surgical procedure does not provide a way to prevent foreign matter from entering the liver, and Alexander soon started suffering complications after his surgery. It was obvious that he needed a liver transplant very soon or he would surely die. After rejecting his first liver transplant, Alexander was lucky enough to be matched up with compatible secondary donor, and this time the operation was a resounding success. Now he was a perfectly healthy and happy two-year-old.

After hearing the story of the Teufel's tribulation and the success story that followed, I felt even more firmly committed to our position that anencephalics should constitute a special category of patient. Surely this man could understand the need to find more sources of donatable organs more than anybody. Surely he could understand our desire for our baby not to needlessly suffer.

But the hosts of the show shied away from directly asking Mr. Teufel on camera whether he agreed with our position or not. Disappointed by their oversight, I asked him for his opinion myself after the taping was over with. He didn't come out and clearly say that he disagreed with us, but it was obvious that he wasn't very enthusiastic about the idea. Like most people out there, he was preoccupied with his own problems, and he wasn't anxious to discuss or deal with the issue. For the most part he sat by in silence when Mary Jo Kahler, the Right-to-Lifer came onto the stage, and the real debate started.

Mary Jo Kahler came out with a rather softened approach compared to most of the RTLers I was used to dealing with, but she was still very critical of the Loma Linda protocol and the idea of using anencephalics as organ donors in general. She started out saying that she had a lot of empathy for people like Mike and me and talked about how many children die from a lack of transplanted organs each year. But then she went on with the classic Right-to-Life argument about how if we make an exception with anencephalics, then the courts are going to interpret it such that irreversibly comatose and other brain-impaired patients are going to be put at risk.

"One thing I think we really need to stress here," I jumped in, "is that anencephalic babies are unique. They are in a category all their own. They are in no way comparable to comatose people or senile patients. There is uncertainty of life in those people. For this baby, there is no past, no present, no future, ... no chance for survival. We don't want to redefine brain death. I would like to see a separate law for anencephalics that, as soon as they are diagnosed as anencephalic, they can become candidates for organ donation as long as that is what the parents wish."

"Mary Jo's problem with that," said one of the co-hosts, "is, again, those perhaps well-meaning, well-intentioned people who might take a little too much license with a very strict or narrow definition of what constitutes brain death and the use of a ventilator and the protocol at Loma Linda. Tell us a little bit about the integrity of the people you dealt with. I'm wondering if you think that they would be able to operate and exist within very narrowly defined parameters."

"I spoke to several Right-to-Life and Pro-Life spokespersons in California," I replied, "and they act like our doctors are mad scientists in a basement, rubbing their hands together while they search for transplantable organs. They say that the doctors are not compassionate. They're robotic. Look at how much money these doctors are going to make from these transplant operations. Loma Linda, by setting this protocol, is doing so at no cost to the patients."

"The University Medical Center will absorb the costs," Mike added.

"They point to where those organs are going," interjected Susan, "and how much money is going to be made apart from you."

"Right. I'm sure my opinion would make a whole lot of difference to the Right-to-Life organization if the life of one of their children was at stake. Everybody is entitled to his or her own opinion. This issue basically depends on a point of view. We're entitled to that, just like they are entitled to their opinion. I don't think that there should be any interference from anybody else."

After a short commercial break, the conversation shifted to Mary Jo Kahler and the Right-to-Life point of view. They asked her point blank that if there was a very narrowly defined category just for anencephalics, could she accept that, if taking the organs from other patients becomes a lot harder.

Mary Jo once again went back to her argument about how the courts might interpret such a law. She quoted a doctor from Loma Linda who said that society couldn't make the distinction between

102

an anencephalic child and a comatose patient. When the co-hosts quizzed her in more detail, she backed off, saying that the topic was very new, and she didn't have time to fully research the issues.

From that point on, the debate began to break down somewhat. I kept insisting that a special category needs to be established, and the Right-to-Lifer kept insisting that the concerns raised by what the courts might do should keep us from moving on the issue. Time was running out, but I think a final comment from Albin Teufel summed up the whole story.

"I hope we haven't lost the common thread here. Each of us believes in the sanctity of life, and we all want to preserve and nurture that, and we are talking about how to accomplish that. I appreciate the need for organs, especially for the very young child, because of the extreme scarcity of available organs. We're trying to find a solution for that. I also want the public to know, since they may not be aware of this, that there is accidental death during normal deliveries. There is a population of usable organs that are probably not being utilized."

CHAPTER XI

When we returned home from Seattle I was frustrated and exhausted. Mike and I fought the whole way back, and I couldn't sleep at all on the plane. Mike was obviously growing tired of my intolerance for the opposition's point of view. His gentle urgings for me to become more accepting soon erupted into full-blown argument. I started lashing out at the RTL crowd and all other the other characters whom I felt had stood in our way. He was more respectful of their opinions.

Maybe he was starting to think that I was too committed to this thing, that I was letting it matter to me too much. But I knew I couldn't kick back and let this story fade into the background as the "experts" gave it more thought. I had to confront these people. Our argument added to my tension level, which was already riding high. Already I was starting to feel the pressure of the next leg of my road trip. In a little more than eighteen hours, I was due right back on a plane to Chicago and the Oprah Winfrey Show. So we were both on nothing but raw nerve when we finally pulled in the driveway that morning and walked in the front door.

There wasn't any time to really relax or unpack, so I just took a quick nap, did a quick change act with my suitcases, took a shower, and that was it. Robin blew in and out for a quick support session, but then it was time to do yet another TV interview. This time it was some airhead corespondent from the local NBC affiliate in Springfield, Missouri. She tried to be nice and follow the script, but a lot of the questions she asked seemed lame-brained and uninformed, but the interview was mercifully short and sweet. Now I had only a short time to prepare before I had to leave for the airport and my big date with Oprah.

My passage on the Oprah Winfrey Redeye Special to Chicago was a strange mix of terror and excitement. I was especially nervous since Mike was not coming along, and I wasn't anxious for my first try as a solo act to be on the road. It felt strange being all alone in the airport at midnight, just me and my little red notebook and a small overnight bag, waiting for my chance to plead my case before the millions. It was a good thing that I had time for some therapeutic talking and crying with Robin before the TV interview that afternoon. At least I wasn't completely without stress release and emotional support. Robin and I were both very good at releasing and sharing our emotions, and our thorough crying session together left me feeling much stronger and determined for the long journey to come.

When I arrived at the airport in Chicago, I spotted a handful of well-dressed men standing outside the airline gate, each holding up a sign with a different name on it. They were obviously waiting to pick up passengers for their limos. Sure enough one of them was holding up a sign with my name on it. As I closed in and identified myself to him, he immediately took my little overnight bag and started to lead the way. He tried to carry my notebook for me, but I wouldn't let go of it. He reached for it once again as we walked out to the parking lot, but I insisted on hanging onto it. I knew he was just playing the game by the rules, but I couldn't help being embarrassed. It was kind of weird to be made a fuss of, and I wasn't taking to it very well at all.

"Just relax, and let us take of you," he kept repeating.

When we reached the limo parked out front, he really started to get irritated when I insisted on sitting up front along side him instead of sitting in the back by myself.

"People are looking at me like I'm somebody important. It's totally embarrassing," I said to him. I was burning up with nervousness, even though I didn't own a heavy winter coat, and it was five below zero in Chicago that morning. Finally he took my camera out of my overnight bag and tried humoring me.

"Why don't you stand in front of the limo," he said, "and I'll take your picture!"

"No, I have a better idea," I answered. "I'll take your picture in front of the limo. If my friends see me in the picture, they'll think I just picked a limo off the street to pose in front of."

Finally, in a desperate attempt to once and for all get me into the back of the limo where I belonged and get us on our way, the limo driver posed for me magnificently, standing proudly before his charge. I snapped a couple pictures, and soon we were on our way to the hotel.

The hotel room Oprah had arranged for me was a first class double way, way up the tower at the Chicago Hilton. I was barely inside the room for fifteen minutes when I realized that it was time to meet Dr. Sherman and Gus Cheatum downstairs for breakfast and a last-minute strategy planning session. Oprah must get an hourly rate on these hotel rooms, I thought to myself.

When I got to breakfast Dr. Sherman and Gus Cheatum were already deeply involved in their game plan and sorting through all the possible contingencies. Dr. Sherman kept talking about how the baboon heart transplant and Baby Faye episode brought on a lot of bad press and how she was determined that it didn't happen again. None of us knew for sure who else was on the discussion panel, but Dr. Sherman kept mentioning Lester Capon, like she was pretty sure he was going to be on with us. Knowing that Capon might be on the show was not much of a comfort to me. I had already heard enough from him on ABC Nightline to last me a lifetime.

Except for a few moments here and there, Dr. Sherman and Gus went on with their intense discussion without seeking any participation on my part. I guess that, in their eyes, I was basically a spectator. So far they were doing a very good job of making me feel like one. Once in a while the flow of the conversation would break, and one of them would turn to me for a five or ten second pep talk.

"Just remember that if you feel nervous, Brenda, and they ask questions you can't answer, we'll be there for you," they took turns telling me.

When we started taping the show, things did not start off well. First of all, none of us got to meet Oprah. We set eyes on her for the first time the precise second that the taping started. There was another couple on the show, Jim and Sally Hahn, who lost their four-month-old while waiting for an organ transplant. A possible anencephalic donor that might have saved him was not used

106

because of the brain death law. What a great pair of guests they would have made, if only they had been allowed a chance to speak. Little did they know, nor did I for that matter, that they were about to be thoroughly steam rolled by the so-called "professionals."

Sure enough Lester Capon was one of the other guests, and he and Dr. Sherman did not take long to lock horns and totally dominate the panel discussion. As their arguing intensified, they started getting more and more off track until finally they began squabbling over small differences in medical terminology and minor legal technicalities.

"Layman's terms, please...," Oprah repeated to them a number of times.

Things were going very badly. I could sense that Oprah was growing to hate the show more and more as each minute passed. I even saw her roll back her eyes a few times in frustration. Every time Oprah or member of the audience tried to ask me or any of the other panelists a question, either Dr. Sherman or Lester Capon, or both, would jump in and start hammering away where they left off. Oprah or someone else would try to direct a question to me, and Dr. Sherman would immediately jump in and attempt to answer it. For example, when Oprah asked me about how we decided that we wanted to donate, I answered that we didn't want to carry her into this world just to bury her. But before I could go on, Dr. Sherman jumped in and said that anencephalic babies are usually discovered at birth where there was no time to make a decision to donate. We were an exception, so the whole donation thing really wasn't a big issue. She seemed determined to downplay our whole story.

It wasn't just me that she would interrupt, but anyone on the panel. She and Mr. Capon seemed to dismiss whatever question was asked. Instead they would simply restate their position or change the subject back to some earlier, unresolved argument. One would go on and on, only to be interrupted by the other. I felt helpless and irrelevant, like I was just an example for them to point at and say, "She's the one who had that brainless baby. So now what do we people who know what we're talking about do about it?"

The true low point, however, came when a few Right-to-Lifers in the audience got up and started telling horror stories about unethical doctors. Over and over the conversation keep switching to the terrible things that they heard that bad doctors do. But the issue of trust in doctors and the medical system had nothing to do with the topic of the show. Once again, I thought to myself, here's proof that these RTL people can't focus on the real issues. I was so tired of people like the Right-to-Lifers shifting the debate over anencephalic donors to the debate over all the horrible things unethical doctors might try to do if we make this one exception to the brain death law.

Even the articulate critics, like Lester Capon, are fixated on the debate of what else anencephalic organ donation might lead to rather than on the facts of the issue itself. It's like underneath it all they secretly have to agree with you, but they are desperate to find a way to keep from admitting it. They try to confuse things by saying that we can't distinguish between anencephalics and other types of terminal patients. To sacrifice anencephalic babies, no matter how much good can result, is construed to put all terminal patients at risk.

Yet at the same time these same people have no trouble recognizing anencephalics as a special category of patients, unlike all other types of terminal patients, when it comes to withholding life support from them. Anencephalics are the only type of terminal patient in which withholding life support is considered to be, almost without question, the most ethical course of action possible. If that doesn't constitute a special category, then what does? Maybe the "experts" can't see it, but the distinction is quite clear to those have held their anencephalic son or daughter in their arms. You simply look to see if there is a brain.

The right questions kept going through my mind as I listened to the others talk, but somehow I couldn't bring myself to speak up and actually ask them. Questions like why does the opposition always imply that every patient on a respirator across the country is going to have their plug pulled if anencephalics are used as organ donors? Why can't people understand that I didn't want my baby to needlessly suffer? Why can't they understand that organ donations add meaning to these babies' lives rather than take it away? Why doesn't anybody count the cost in terms of the lives being lost while everyone wrings their hands over this?

Every time I got close to speaking up, I pulled back. After all the only reason that I was here was because of the protocol — the Loma Linda University Medical Center protocol. I couldn't embarrass Dr. Sherman by publicly bringing up sticky issues or openly questioning the wisdom of her approach. That would only destroy what modest achievements we had managed to scrounge together up to this point.

I was frustrated. How could I ask anybody the real questions? How can you make people understand something when they don't have to or don't want to? Why should they care if it's not their baby who is anencephalic? It's not their baby who needs an organ transplant to survive. Do we call it "comfort care" because we need to comfort those poor dying babies or because we need instead to comfort ourselves?

And even though the show was going terribly for Oprah, who constantly had to round up the audience participants who kept drifting off onto different subjects, I sensed that most of the people weren't buying the message that people like Lester Capon were delivering. I could sense an underlying ground swell within the audience, no matter how repressed it might seem. I started feeling better about the show as it became obvious that, for the most part, the audience was siding with my point of view. Maybe I didn't have to run off at the mouth to make my point after all. But I knew that all was not lost when one audience member in particular stood and said her peace in front of the cameras.

"I'm a Right-to-Life member," she said, "and I think what they're trying to do is life. If I had a baby that needed a transplant, I would be thankful for their decision!"

Her statement brought on a resounding round of applause from the studio audience.

I was scheduled to do another radio interview in Chicago after the taping with Oprah. I hopped a ride with my favorite limo driver. This time I just jumped right in the back — with no arguments. The producer of the radio talk show was a former Oprah Winfrey staff member, which he assured me was not a very exclusive country club. In typical Chicago style, he did not offer his former boss warm praise or even much kindness.

"How did it feel to come to Chicago on an airplane as big as the talk show host who provided it," he opened as we shook hands. Of course I laughed.

"We aren't big Oprah fans around here, and we never will be!" he added.

The radio show was easy compared to what I had just been through. It was just me and the DJ and the callers. There was no panel or audience. The callers we talked to were sympathetic, for the most part, and offered me a lot of praise and support. Although

I was extremely tired at this point, I greatly appreciated the kind words of those callers. The radio producer gave me a tape of interviews he made with various people on the streets of Chicago to take home with me. Afterwards I got a whirlwind tour of the city as the limo driver and I killed an hour. Then I left on a plane for back home.

The next day after I arrived home, I received a call from a woman by the name of Carnel Sessoms, who was the producer of a local television show in Detroit called "Kelly and Company." They invited Mike and me to fly out to Detroit for an interview at their expense. We were to be interviewed live on the air. Mike and I jumped at the offer, and a tentative date for our appearance — January 29th, was set.

The feverish pace of my recent travels was starting to take its toll on me, and the touch of bronchitis that I developed before I left on the last two road trips now had me on the ropes. One night I was so bad that Mike took me to the emergency room down at Arcadia Methodist Hospital. Fortunately things quieted down, and I only received one interview request the entire next week. I needed time to nurse myself back to mental health, as well regain my physical strength. But I got lucky when my sister Dori arrived to look after me and keep me company for a few days. It was great having a kind, devoted sister like her around to take care of me, even if it was for only a short while.

The next day I finished a low-key but gratifying interview with Shauna Vogel of Discover magazine. She was very forthcoming and warm, and I knew her article would be a good one. She seemed to be much more sophisticated and articulate than the TV hacks I was used to. I guess she was shooting for a better educated, better informed audience. I also did a live interview with WCKY radio in Cincinnati. Just when I was getting into a good mood, I found a copy of the latest issue of Time magazine while on a trip to the grocery store. Dated February 1, it contained an article titled "A Balancing Act of Life and Death" that attacked the use of fetal tissue for transplantation to patients with Parkinson's disease. In a very slanted and misleading way, the article lumped together the idea of using anencephalics as organ donors with the sale of tissue from aborted and miscarried fetuses.

The most misleading part of all was the image of a normal, intact, developing fetus featured prominently in the center of the article. The photograph suggested that anencephalic infants really look the same as any normal fetus, even though in the fine print they described what an anencephalic really looks like. The way they lumped together these two topics, anencephalic organ donors and tissue transplants involving tissue from aborted fetuses, seemed inexcusable to me. They didn't treat anencephalic organ donors like they would any other category of organ donor. No, that was too subtle a distinction for them to grasp.

Here, after all the bullshit we've been through with how we must protect the dignity and humanity of the anencephalic infant at all costs, Time magazine had no problem with categorizing our baby as just another aborted fetus. Not only did they suggest that Mike and I were in the same category as organ peddlers, but they also had no trouble equating my baby to a dehumanized lump of surplus fetal tissue. Anencephalics were just an upscale version of an aborted fetus, or so it seemed from the Time article. The implication was that parents like us want to casually cast our baby aside for whatever reason, including the possibility of picking up a few quick bucks.

I bitterly resented the inference that what Mike and I chose to do with Jarren was the moral equivalent of selling tissue from aborted fetuses in sort of an organ factory type of scenario. The article also contained a very thinly veiled swipe at both Loma Linda and "parents of anencephalics" — namely Mike and me. It sent me into a fury. To read something like this now, after Time magazine gave me their big suck-up routine before the baby was born, left me incensed. This was even dirtier than the sudden brush off they gave me in December when they found out that Jarren was stillborn and a successful transplant was no longer possible.

How dare they equate the Loma Linda protocol to the cultivation and sale of fetal tissue for personal gain? The more I thought about it, the angrier I became. The two subjects were entirely unrelated. Fetal tissue transplants have nothing to do with brain death or brain absence. We weren't selling baby parts. We didn't abort any babies. We weren't out for any profit or gain. We didn't plan this. Why didn't that article mention Baby Paul and the good things that could come out of using anencephalics as organ donors? I am so sick of sensational rags like Time magazine showcasing only one side of an issue and then conning their readers into thinking they're getting the whole truth.

It was just so typical for those jokers at Time to pull something like this. After my experiences with them, I should have guessed by now what their recipe for "the news" is all about. Mixing up cheap shots is their specialty. You take any story, put a healthy spin on it, mix it with the right amount of exaggeration and disinformation, and then lightly season it with a delicate blend of rumor and innuendo. Voila! You have a Time magazine. That's what these people are all about — highly polished and processed pieces of truth. They're white rice, and never mind that the world needs more bran. How can so many intelligent people buy and believe a low-class rag like that?

In a somewhat soothing but futile gesture, I took all the copies of Time magazine from the magazine rack and took them with me into the store. In every aisle, every nook and cranny, anywhere I could find, I stashed Time magazines so that no one could either see one, find one, or buy one. I even stuck a few in the freezer case. This was a practice that I was to repeat over and over again in the coming months. I was so angry that I even had some of my friends doing it. It had to have cost them at least a few sales. Insinuate that I'm a fetal tissue peddler out for my own gain will you? Well, I'll show you Time magazine!

When I got home, I took out all the phone numbers I had for people at Time. They were going to hear about this one. I dialed the number for Jim Willwerth. He was the reporter who did our original interview. He wasn't in at his office number, of course, but he had made a critical mistake. In his haste to show his compassion and concern for our situation back in December, he left his home phone number with me. Of course he told me to call anytime day or night. I was about to take him up on that.

When I dialed his home phone number, his wife answered. If Jim was there, he wasn't in the mood to talk, and his poor wife got stuck covering for him. By this time I was nearly hysterical, pulling myself together between bouts of crying only long enough to unload some serious grief on my captive audience. Mrs. Willwerth was actually very nice, and she seemed sympathetic, although she was being forced to do her husband's bidding for him. She kept telling me that she knew how I felt, but that it was out of Jim's hands and there was nothing he could do. After all, it wasn't even his story. I didn't bother to tell her that I saw his name included on the article's byline.

After realizing that I was going nowhere by harassing this innocent and unsuspecting woman, I finally let her off the hook and hung up the phone. I dialed up the magazine's headquarters and talked to Jim's boss, the story editor. I gradually climbed all the way up the management ladder of Time magazine, until I finally got the editor-in-chief of the whole magazine himself on the phone. I gave him a dose of my complaints, which I was sure were now circulating around every coffee machine in the Time-Life building. He listened very politely, but then he gave me only one brief answer.

"Mrs. Winner, the only thing I care about is whether Time magazine is getting published...."

A few days later, I got a call from a Right-to-Lifer who had seen the Time article. She insisted that because the picture they published with the article was of an intact fetus, it proved that there was nothing really wrong with anencephalic babies after all. I guess I should have given the writers at Time more credit – it was their readers who were the real idiots.

Enough was enough. I decided to write a letter to the editor at Time to voice my complaint and leave it at that. Hopefully they would be decent enough to at least publish my letter. There was nothing else I could do. By the February 29th issue of Time, my letter to the editor was published (edited to their satisfaction, of course), and that was the end of it.

Mike and I left for our appearance on Kelly and Company in Detroit on January 28th. We got there early in the morning, and we went straight to the studio to do the taping. One of the other guests was Martin Benjamin, a University of Michigan philosophy professor who wrote a medical protocol that allows anencephalics to be declared brain dead at birth. This was a man after my own heart. But an even more impressive guest than Dr. Benjamin was also on the show that day. He was Dr. Mark Evans, a doctor who intentionally aborted six octuplets in one of his pregnant patients in order to save the remaining two. There also was another panel member, a Right-to-Lifer whose name I can't remember. I braced myself for some big time shock waves.

One of the first topics we talked about was a new, controversial amendment to Michigan's brain death law. Dr. Benjamin headed a panel of ethicists, religious leaders, and private citizens who drafted the amendment that would allow physicians to declare anencephalics as brain dead at birth. He used the analogy of a tearing down a building to explain the difference between taking a comatose patient off life support and removing the organs from an anencephalic infant. If you never see anyone

113

come in or out of building, you can't be sure that nobody's home, even if there's no light on inside. You can't tear it down without a chance of killing someone. But if the building has no roof, or is missing a wall or two, then you can see inside. You know with certainty that nobody's home. Anencephalics are like that building with no roof; it's OK to take their organs since you know that there is no one left inside.

Things were quiet so far, but I think it was because Dr. Benjamin's analogy went over the heads of most of the people in the audience. But things really started heating up when the attention turned to Dr. Evans and the story of one of his patients who was pregnant with octuplets. The debate was over whether it was the right choice to abort six of the fetuses to save two, as Dr. Evans and his patient decided to do, or let all eight survive to full term and be stillborn or be born severely underdeveloped. But to top it off, they also had a woman by the name of Patty Crustacy connected up live on the telephone. Patty herself had been pregnant with octuplets, but went the other way with it and decided to carry all eight to full term. However, those who survived were severely handicapped as a result.

At first it sounds incredibly cold and callous to eliminate multiple fetuses so that the survivors have a reasonable chance of developing. But after hearing Patty describe the results of her pregnancy, I could understand why Dr. Evans and his patient went through with the abortions. Of the eight fetuses only six lived through childbirth. All six are totally blind, four are severely retarded, and it takes almost a million dollars a year to take care of them all. I couldn't imagine coping in that situation. I would totally lose it. Even more fascinating was her comment that, given the same circumstances, she would do the same thing again.

The reason she gave for her decision was that she couldn't decide whom to kill. I guess I can see her point. But two of the babies died despite her decision to try to save all of them. So is the trade off that Dr. Evans and his patient made in forming their decision really that different? It wasn't hard to tell whose side the Right-to-Lifer was on, and Patty's phone call was a sort of spring board to action for an anti-abortion propaganda blitzkrieg. But it was the same old line about protecting the rights of the babies and stopping unethical transplant doctors. The audience wasn't taking to it, and I felt the momentum turn our way.

It's no wonder that most people don't buy the Chicken Little Theory when it comes to an anencephalic organ donor. The Right-to-Lifers go on and on about the baby's rights, but what these people really want is the right to impose their decision-making power on my baby and me. They want to expand their rights and their power, not protect or preserve my rights or my baby's rights. They love to conjure up images of greedy doctors and unscrupulous parents and turn this thing into the threat of a new criminal industry because it makes for great scare tactics. By claiming the whole thing is a conspiracy by the doctors and the donors to harvest baby parts and to pad their wallets, they can escape facing the real issues and the real people behind the story.

The audience seemed even more supportive as Mike and I started to tell our story. The Right-to-Lifer on the panel must have sensed she was losing ground and got even more zealous and nasty.

"What did you name that baby anyway?" she interrupted, as Mike was talking to one of the co-hosts of the show.

"Jarren," Mike calmly answered.

"Doesn't that mean 'garbage' or something? Isn't that what you're treating her like?" she sneered.

"No," Mike replied, "Jarren is derived from 'Jarrod' which means 'descendant.' She was sent to us to make us more aware of people like you!"

What a bitch, I thought to myself. The audience was dead quiet. They must have been in shock. These Right-to-Life people were some piece of work. I guess if you're too ignorant to make a stand on the issues, the "Christian" thing to do is launch personal attacks.

After the show was over, a friend of the Right-to-Lifer on the panel came up to Mike and me and apologized for her companion's rude behavior on stage. It wasn't the most sincere of apologies that I ever received, seeing how the panelist herself stood off at a discrete distance, quietly pouting away in a huff. I don't get it. These people consider themselves to be so moral and just, yet they can't even handle a little common courtesy. But we both knew who won the debate. I guess all she had left were cheap shots.

I also had the chance to talk privately with Dr. Benjamin after the show. It was so comforting and reassuring to know that there were enlightened and intelligent men like him interested in this issue. He suggested that I write a book about our experiences. What better way was there to continue our fight and to answer all the critics? Jarren needs our determination to help others was his message.

On February 11th, I did an interview with the Toronto Star News. The Cincinnati Enquirer also called me on the phone. They wanted to know my reaction to the news that a hospital in Akron was going to use the protocol to help a couple that wanted to donate their anencephalic baby's organs. I told them that I was delighted. How else was I going to react? I told them I would send them copies of both the LLUMC protocol and the Martin Benjamin protocol to help them research their article.

The next few days were tough ones for me health-wise. I had another asthma attack. This one was more severe than the last episode, and Mike had to take me to the emergency room at Arcadia Methodist Hospital. It was very bad. They ended up letting me go home that night. My spirits were finally lifted again, however, when I got home and received a phone call from the Good Day Show in Boston. They wanted Mike and me to fly in for a taping in early March. This was exciting. Even though it was just another local morning show, I had never been to Boston, and the producers were obviously very interested in the topic. Of course I immediately accepted their offer.

A few days later Mike and I appeared on the Los Angeles equivalent of the Good Day Show, a morning program called AM Los Angeles or, in California lingo, AM LA. The producers had also invited Dr. Platt as a guest, and we were chatting backstage when a very pretty woman in an expensive dress came up to us and introduced herself. It was Christina Ferrari, the famous model and current co-host of AM LA. She was also famous for being married to (and divorced from) John DeLorean. Even though she was wearing heavy stage makeup, she was still incredibly beautiful, and her presence left me a little star struck.

Christina kept periodically giving Dr. Platt these strange looks as the four of us conversed. It seemed a little odd to me, but then finally she interrupted herself and asked, "Dr. Platt, have we met before?"

Dr. Platt fidgeted uncomfortably for a moment. "I'm your gynecologist," he answered simply.

We kind of laughed, and obviously Christina was somewhat embarrassed about not recognizing her own gynecologist.

"Oh, I didn't recognize you without your white coat!" she added.

I didn't really appreciate the humor of the moment at the time. I guess I felt embarrassed for her as well. But it did reassure me that even the rich and famous can sometimes lose touch with the simple facts of their lives.

We cut the small talk and quickly headed for the sound stage. It was a sedate environment for an interview, and sedate could have been the theme for the entire interview. At least it all seemed very sedate to me. I was getting frustrated. After all the talk, the hype, and the publicity, things were not moving forward. I was just saying and doing the same things over and over, but with less and less results. Even though I was getting a nice round of applause or two, applause was not what this battle was all about. Now I have my routine down pat. Officially I back the Loma Linda protocol word-for-word, at least when I'm pressured into taking a stand in front of the national media. But I didn't really agree with it, and those feeling were coming out all over the place in these interviews. It was too subtle for the public to really take notice, but basically I was contradicting myself.

Even if I could convince myself that I did wholeheartedly agree with the Loma Linda protocol, the protocol was, at the very least, holding at a standstill. After nearly two months, no other anencephalic babies besides Jarren had participated in the program. With the Tucker bill to ban the protocol now pending in Sacramento, we could all find ourselves backpedaling real fast any time now. I was getting worried. We had reached a point where we had all flash and no substance, yet our flash was also quickly fading.

CHAPTER XII

The call from Loma Linda came on the morning of February 17th. An anencephalic infant, named Baby John, had been born earlier in the day, and was being admitted to Loma Linda under the protocol at the parent's request. I was elated. This turn of events meant that there was at least one other family out there willing to go through with the organ donation; maybe this was the breakthrough we had been waiting for. I told Loma Linda to call me and let me know the minute there was any more news.

Baby John was a local baby from somewhere in Southern California, although they either couldn't or wouldn't tell me exactly where he was from. After 25 hours on the ventilator he was determined to meet brain death. A worldwide search was immediately launched for compatible recipients. Despite the fact that Baby John lived out the entire seven days of the protocol, and the search for potential recipients was exhaustive, no compatible recipient was found. After the seventh day, Baby John was taken off life support. He died immediately thereafter. The protocol had come close, but no cigar!

Just the fact that we were no longer the only couple to have participated in the LLUMC protocol made me feel a lot better about our prospects for the future. Either my letter writing campaign had been effective, or somebody else was also lobbying behind the scenes, because on February 18th State Senator Art Torres introduced a bill into the California State Legislature affirming the legality of the protocol. If it passed, the bill would ensure that the protocol would stay legal with the full authority of a written statute behind it. Things were looking up. We decided we needed to at least try to lobby for the bill in Sacramento. We needed to contact anybody in the capital that would listen. Assemblyman Tucker's bill to outlaw the protocol could not go unchallenged.

It was only two days later, when I received word from Loma Linda that the parents of a third anencephalic baby had requested their baby participate in the protocol. The baby's name was Baby Evelyn, and she was flown into Loma Linda on a special chartered flight from Texas on February 20th. Now there was yet another chance for the protocol to go somewhere. This time, however, I was more cautious about getting my hopes up.

After more than two days on the ventilator, Baby Evelyn still had not met the brain death criteria. We were invited out to Loma Linda to speak at a grief counseling session on the third day. This was one of three or four sessions we were to participate in over the next few months. To my surprise, there were no other grieving parents, but rather Mike and I found ourselves standing in front of an audience of bright young medical students. A pastor of the Seventh Day Adventist Church, the founding organization of Loma Linda University and its Medical Center led the discussion. The first thing that he told us was that they were all very surprised by how well we had handled our grief, and they were very curious as to the reasons why. "What makes you 'atypical'?" as the pastor put it to us.

So once again I told the story of my early pregnancy and ultrasound test, as well as our fight to challenge the brain death law and donate our baby's organs. I described the birth of my daughter, Jarren, and the birth of the LLUMC protocol. Afterwards I told them that the key to handling the grief, at least for me, was education. Whether it was through books, or doctors, or by word-of-mouth, I had to educate myself about what was happening to me. The worst part of the whole situation, I explained to them, was having people ask me "What is anencephaly?" and then not have an answer for them. Instead of crying, I used information gathering as a catharsis. I had to search for the real meaning of what happened to us, and that process bonded me to my baby, even if I was the only one who understood the real reasons for her short life on this Earth. It was my way of showing Jarren that I wasn't going to give up on her.

The grief counseling session went very well, and I think that I got as much out of the discussion as the med students did. I guess I shouldn't let my frustrations with Dr. Sherman taint my whole attitude toward LLUMC. Most of the people there were really quite nice. And even though I did my best to get the media to pressure Loma Linda into doing something about anencephalic organ donors and the brain death law, it's not like they had to cave in to any of it. They could have just turned their backs on Mike and me altogether, just like all the rest of the doctors and hospitals. Maybe I was being too harsh in my assessment of these people. But if I wasn't grateful to them, then why was I always toeing the LLUMC party line? Why was I pushing the protocol so hard, when the way I really want things is different?

When I got home from Loma Linda, I received a call from an editor at USA Today. They wanted me to write a guest editorial for the opinion page of their next edition. I sat down and wrote down my article by hand and then phoned it in the next day. It was titled "Something So Right Can't Be Wrong." It was published on February 25th. The entire opinion page was devoted to the issue of anencephalic organ donors. They published a short article by Arthur Caplan, the University of Minnesota ethicist, entitled "Don't Let Baseless Fears Block This Choice." A Right-to-Life member wrote the counterpoint article, titled "Stop the Transplants — It's Playing with Death." They also had an attending quotation from Lester Capon reading "What they are doing here I think is an indication of the danger that these babies are being regarded as another species."

Needless to say I had no trouble deciding whose viewpoint I agreed with. Also needless to say I collected numerous copies of that issue of USA Today for my friends and myself. It was probably the only USA Today that I had ever purchased. But as I glanced through the other articles and features on the page, I was also struck by one of the comments I saw quoted in a box underneath my editorial.

One of USA Today's special features is a poll of six people chosen at random on a particular subject of the day. They include a photograph of each person with their response quoted underneath. The topic for the February 25th issue was the question "Should organs from brain dead babies be used for transplants?" One woman, named Liz Ruiz, responded "When you don't have a child who's sick, you don't realize how important organ donation is." I could agree more, Liz!

I called Dr. Arthur Caplan at the University of Minnesota, and touched base with him on our situation and the state of the LLUMC protocol. He was a very nice man, and was very supportive, although he couldn't offer me much more than a boost in confidence. He seemed more reasonable than the people with tight shorts. Although Dr. Caplan's stance was more conservative than the one Mike and I advocated, he still basically saw the protocol as sensible and harmless to society. He also saw it as an issue dealing with personal choice, an argument that always seemed lost on the opposition.

No sooner than when I hung up with Dr. Caplan, than the phone immediately rang again. It was those clowns from People Magazine again. I guess they don't take no for an answer. Despite all my refusals to consent to an interview or have anything else to do with them, they still called me about once a month to see if I ever changed my mind. I told them that I was still not interested, but the reporter could help but interject "Are you going to have a baby again right away? Please call us if you do...."

By the end of her seventh day, February 28th, Baby Evelyn still had not met the brain death criteria. As called for in the LLUMC protocol, she was taken off of life support, and she died shortly thereafter.

Another painful disappointment had been suffered, and it was becoming obvious by now that establishing the protocol had only been the easy part. Making it work was going to be a lot tougher. Although it was still early, the more failures that piled up the more likely it was that the protocol would be suspended or even canceled outright. Still I was determined to keep the faith. I continued with my mailing campaign to send anyone I could think of my personal letter with a copy of the protocol enclosed.

About a week later, on March 9th, we were supposed to leave for our appearance on Good Day, Boston, but I came down sick again at the last minute. We had to reschedule the show for May 6th. The next day another anencephalic infant was born in Southern California, this time down in Anaheim south of Los Angeles in Orange County. Her name was Baby Dee, and her parents consented to immediately placing her on life support according to the protocol. Two days later Baby Cassandra was flown in from Texas to also participate in the protocol. Both babies lived the entire seven days while on the respirator, but neither baby was determined to meet brain death before the weeklong deadline expired. Both babies also died almost immediately after being taken off life support.

The pressure building up on Loma Linda over its protocol had been growing fast enough on its own, but now that two more "failures" were added to the political balance sheet, something was bound to give. The critics of the protocol were now focused on the possibility that the protocol was "unnecessarily" extending the life span of anencephalics. Given the cases of Baby Evelyn, Baby Dee, and Baby Cassandra, maybe they were right. But the critics ignored the fact that Baby John had met brain death while on the protocol, and it was only because of bad luck in finding a recipient that a successful transplant could not take place.

We decided that we had to go to Sacramento and make our voices heard on the Assembly Floor, if only we could get them to let us in. We had a good start in that I had received responses to some of the letters I had written to various representatives on the subject earlier in the year. Three of them, Art Torres, Diane Watson, and Sally Tanner agreed to meet with us in the state capital to discuss both the Torres and Tucker bills.

On March 22nd, Mike, Christi, and I left on our trip to Sacramento. Hearings on the Tucker bill to outlaw the LLUMC protocol were due to begin the next day. Early the next afternoon, we met with Sally, Diane, and Art in his office in the State Capital. We did our best to talk them into getting us in to speak on the floor. They seemed very happy to talk to supporters of a bill, but beyond talk, they seemed willing to do little else.

Something else that bothered me was the way Senator Torres never took his eyes off Christi's legs — not even for a minute. Somehow after that experience it wasn't much of a surprise to me when a few years later the Feds busted our buddy Art on corruption charges. So either to placate a few agitated constituents, to allow Art a chance to get a better angle on Christi's legs, or both, they took us all out to dinner. We had a good time, but it was all smoke and mirrors. It looked like we weren't going to get results. Lucky for us, however, it didn't matter. After collecting dust for a couple weeks on the assembly's docket, Tucker's bill ended up being delayed over a technicality. Later that year it was thrown off the assembly floor completely for undisclosed reasons.

On April 1st, Baby Hope was born to couple in Knoxville, Tennessee. She had an unusual form of anencephaly, called merocrania, and she was flown to California to participate in the protocol on April 3rd. But because she still had some cornea reflexes, she didn't meet brain death for the weeklong duration of the protocol. Later, when I found out the details surrounding her birth from reading a Knoxville newspaper article about her, I was amazed by how similar her parents' situation had been compared to what Mike and I had been through.

Like Mike and me, the Mounts were informed of their baby's condition after a routine ultrasound exam during the fifth month of her pregnancy. Like Mike and me, the Mounts also chose not to abort their baby. Like me, Kay wasn't ready for her pregnancy to be over just like that. Like me, Kay didn't want to see or hold her baby at first, but then later changed her mind after the baby was born.

After Baby Hope was born, the Mounts tried to find someone who would accept their baby's organs for transplantation. They knew about Loma Linda and the protocol, but at first they were reluctant to participate because the protocol called for keeping the infant on a respirator at all times. They were worried about causing their baby unnecessary discomfort. But after contacting Loma Linda and requesting that the respirator be used only when she had trouble breathing on her own, Loma Linda agreed to their terms. LLUMC sent their Lear jet out to Knoxville to fly the baby out to California.

Baby Hope did not meet brain death during her weeklong stay at Loma Linda under the protocol. But when they took Baby Hope off life support altogether, something totally unexpected happened. She continued to live for another nine weeks, even without the benefit of a respirator. Baby Hope was somewhat unique in that she had more brain tissue than the average anencephalic baby did. She also had strong corneal and sucking reflexes, and even had some hearing capability. Whether she lived so long because of the protocol or whether she would have lived that long anyway was an open question. Every case of anencephaly was different, and anything was possible.

But because of the length of the period of time that she lived, many were assuming that the week of intensive care Baby Hope had received during the protocol had unnecessarily prolonged her life and her suffering. Even Dr. Sherman was being forced to admit that a pattern was emerging. After all, Hope was the fifth protocol baby to show signs that supported such a theory. The pressure to revise or eliminate the protocol altogether was now building to a crescendo. I was convinced more than ever that the best way to avoid all these questions and theories was to go back to our original request — that the baby's organs be removed at birth.

On April 13th, LLUMC announced that it was revising the protocol for its anencephalic organ donor program. The new procedure allows for providing assistance to anencephalic participants only after signs of distress are observed. Although technically this was the version of the protocol that was used with Baby Hope, the changes were now official. Partly because of the negative publicity over the protocol's lagging success rate, and partly because the story was getting very stale, the news media took little interest in this new development. In fact, it was hardly mentioned most places, although CNN did call me to get my reaction to the announcement. Except for the Good Day, Boston show coming up in May, it seemed I had basically shot my wad with the media, and either they didn't care anymore or they just plain weren't interested.

From about mid-April on, I hung on dearly to what was left of my hopes for the protocol. I had reached a point where I was blindly hopeful, even though all of the attention had quieted around me. Near the end of the month I was invited to USC to accept an award at a symposium given by the Anatomical Transplant Association of California. The award was given out annually to outstanding private citizens that have aided organ transplants, and it was presented to us by SCOPPC. We also presented a plaque of our own to Loma Linda's Dr. Bailey in appreciation for all his hard work in the area of pediatric organ transplants. It was nice to receive some recognition, but still an award was pretty superficial accomplishment compared to saving someone's life.

On May 6th we left for Massachusetts and our appearance on Good Day, Boston. The show went better than anything else Mike and I did before, and the positive feedback from most of the audience was incredible. The Right-to-Life was also in the audience, and as usual they were very vocal. But they were outnumbered, and it was clear that many people still cared about the issue and were interested in the debate. Many of them were strong supporters of our position. It was the kind of triumph that kept my hopes alive and my spirit kicking. Maybe the media at large was no longer interested, but the grass roots support was still there. It helped me keep putting off the lingering feeling I had deep down inside that the protocol was in serious trouble.

On June 3rd Baby Erin was admitted to Loma Linda as the seventh brain-absent infant to participate in the protocol. Little mention was made of her, even in the local newspapers. She was cared for under the new guidelines, and she died the very next day. Her organs were considered too damaged from lack of oxygen to be successfully transplanted.

Baby Erin set a pattern that was to be repeated for the remaining anencephalic babies whom participated in the LLUMC protocol. Loma Linda would always call and let me know when a new baby came in, but I would never hear a thing on the news or read anything in the newspaper. They were taken care of under the new guidelines of the altered protocol, and they typically died within a day or two of entering the program.

The reason for the poor results obtained under the new Loma Linda guidelines was the extreme demands of care management imposed by the need to monitor the babies for distress. The monitoring had to be done constantly and at least some of the babies had to have died because life support was withheld for too long a period of time before distress was identified.

I had made friends with one of the nurses in the neonatal ward at LLUMC, and I would periodically talk to her on the phone about the latest situation. She told me that even some of the physicians were getting anxious about continuing the protocol. They were frustrated because the babies were suffering and dying at tremendous emotional and financial cost, and so far there was nothing to show for their efforts. I was a little upset to hear this news, because if the professionals were having trouble handling the situation, how could I expect everyone else to act?

The all-time clincher came a month later when I heard through my nurse friend that the tenth baby to participate in the protocol had been determined to meet brain death. An immediate search had begun to a recipient, and incredibly, this time they found a suitable patient. The only hang up was that the staff could not proceed with anything until Dr. Sherman arrived at the hospital. She had left strict orders that the organ removal could only be done if she was personally present, and no one else was to even attempt it without her being there to supervise.

The difficulty was that Dr. Sherman lived near Big Bear Lake, which is a two to three hour drive from Loma Linda. By the time Dr. Sherman arrived, it was too late, and the baby's organs had atrophied. I had to wonder if the situation turned out the way it did by design rather than by accident. I always had the impression that Dr. Sherman wanted the protocol dead, buried, and forgotten, and the sooner the better. Here was a perfect opportunity, and she seemed almost deliberately willing to throw it away.

The worst of it was that Dr. Sherman used this incident to set a final ultimatum on the protocol. If the next patient to enter the protocol resulted in a successful transplant, she decreed, then the program would continue intact. But if a successful transplant did not result, the whole show was over, and the protocol would be suspended altogether. I thought it rather arbitrary and unfair that Dr. Sherman to pin the whole program on the success or failure of single case. It did support my theory, however, that Dr. Sherman was looking for an excuse to cancel the whole thing. In my opinion, she wasn't interested in making the protocol work.

It was almost a year to the day from when I first found out I was carrying an anencephalic fetus, on August 23rd, that I made one last trip out to Loma Linda. The last baby to participate in the protocol — the eleventh in all — had died a couple weeks earlier. I didn't hear anything right away, so I assumed that maybe Dr. Sherman had changed her mind. She seemed perfectly calm and natural when I caught her in her office, like nothing out of the ordinary was in the works. When I asked her for more copies of the protocol, she obliged me quietly, without mentioning a word of what was to come. It wasn't until the next morning when I received a phone call from Selwyn Eiber, the reporter from the Pasadena Star News, that I found out that Dr. Sherman was calling a news conference to announce the suspension of the protocol.

Later that day CNN came by and picked us up on their way to the news conference at Loma Linda. As Dr. Sherman answered questions from the press, I stood and asked her one of my own.

"Dr. Sherman," I asked, sobbing with my eyes full of tears, "why is the protocol being suspended when it has only been in effect for six months?"

"Now Brenda," Dr. Sherman responded, "remember I told you from the beginning that if anyone had any emotional difficulty whatsoever with the protocol that it would be terminated immediately."

Her answer, of course, left me unsatisfied. Was she saying that some of the doctors were having a difficult time dealing with the protocol? Was that why they were suspending it? None of the parents were objecting, at least not from what I had been hearing. I thought she meant that if the parents were having "emotional difficulties" that would cause the protocol to be suspended, not because some of the doctors were uncomfortable with it. But then did Dr. Sherman really need a good excuse to terminate the protocol?

Although I was extremely disappointed, the events of the previous day at Loma Linda seemed like a fitting ending to the yearlong ordeal Mike and I had suffered through. There I was, right in Dr. Sherman's office, and she didn't even give me a hint as to what was really going on with the protocol. It was so typical of her to snub me like that, even though I had tirelessly spent the last six months campaigning for what she had ostensibly claimed as her own cause. But then I guess it was never really her cause anyway.

The final picture truly gelled when I spoke one more time to my friend on the LLUMC nursing staff. She said that now that the protocol had been in effect for six months, Dr. Sherman could still receive credit for it as a successful protocol and publish it, even though it was no longer in effect. It was now obvious to me that Dr. Sherman was willing to put up with the protocol for as long as she did mainly to accomplish her own professional purposes, and now that she didn't need it anymore, she could happily wish it good riddance forever.

EPILOGUE

The years have passed by now, and my memories of the protocol and all the people involved are starting to fade. But it is rare for a day to pass by that I don't think of Jarren. I have my memories of her and my fading scrapbook of newspaper clippings and photos, but I still can't help but cling to thoughts of what might have been. I think of what it would be like to see her smile for the first time or take her first steps. I think of Jarren whenever I see a toddler reaching out for Mommy or when I see a kid crying because he didn't get to pet the doggy that just walked by his stroller. It's funny the way your mind plays games with you. To this day I still stop to look at the price tags on the baby clothes when I go to the mall, or I pick out which toys in the display window of the department stores I would buy for her if things had turned out differently. I feel like I owe her a gift, you know, for all the wonderful things she gave me with the short time we had together. I owe her something for that special strength and courage she gave me just by being there inside me, the faithful companion who never left me — 'til death do us part. I had to think of what I would give her, if I had the chance to bestow just that one final gift.

A friend suggested to me that I write her a letter, a kind of farewell message containing all the things I would say to her if I had that one chance to sit down with her and chat. I thought that was a wonderful idea, but I had so much to say I hardly knew where to start. I guess it didn't really matter if I could think of everything. What was important was that I find a way to share my feelings; somehow or some way the words might reach her the same way a prayer reaches up to heaven. Writing has been a good way for me to release and share my feelings; the same way this book has been a way to share my feelings with you. Perhaps we know each other, or perhaps we are strangers. It doesn't matter. By me writing this and you reading it, I feel like I've formed so many new and wonderful bonds, close bonds, a meeting of our minds and spirits outside those barriers of space and time that separate us. So why not try to do the same thing with Jarren? It made perfect sense. So I had a few goes at it, and here's what I finally ended up settling on:

Dear Jarren,

I sit here with so many thoughts of you, so many questions. You, my sweet baby girl, will forever be on my mind. I'm so thankful for the time we had together. I only wish that it could have been forever. I must admit, my darling, I'm not quite as strong without you, but you have left me strong enough to continue our battle to change an injustice that still continues to cost so much in wasted lives. As I sit here and reflect over the past, I realize that your life was not wasted. I am amazed at how much you've shown to so many people, and how much I've learned thanks to you. I also realize how tough our journey together has been, and I will not forget as I continue our battle how tough our quest will continue to be. I can carry on now without you because you helped me find the strength inside me I never knew I had. It is because of you that I will fight that much harder. It is because of you that I can stand a little taller, and it is because of you that I now know what it means to feel powerful in what seems to be a powerless situation.

They told me that you were neither perfect nor complete, but to me you will always be both. Now I know that it is only this world that God kept you from that is neither perfect nor complete. So many looked at you as only another tragedy. You were just a terrible mistake to them, something that could be corrected by simply trying again. But it is really the world that has suffered a tragedy. It is the world that must try again. I will always know that

129

the world is emptier and more flawed without you in your place in my arms. It is a world that desperately needs people like you who can contribute to the changes that will bring us all closer to harmony and perfection.

You've done so much in so little time, my little angel. In just four short months you made people listen and hear and take notice – and you did it all by just being here, without making speeches, without making protests, without doing any more than showing to me and the world those beautiful fingers of yours, your ten perfect fingers. I was told not to interfere with your rights, to let you die with dignity. Please believe me, my beloved daughter, that I cherish nothing more than your rights. Nothing meant more to me than for your life to end with dignity. That's why I wouldn't settle for comfort care for you – nothing seemed more undignified and cruel to me. I knew you would be afraid and would suffer terribly. I hope you understand why I could not let that happen. I hope you understand that I wanted more for you than just a fancy new protocol for the doctors to publish, more than just a ventilator and a blanket to keep you warm.

Thank you, my wonderful baby girl, for adding such meaning to my life. I know that you have made me a better human being. Thank you for exposing a terrible and foolish injustice to me, instead of letting me go on like so many others unable to see or feel the tragedies around me and forget the difference we can make if we only try. I see now how much I've taken for granted, like the feelings of your life growing within me and the fearlessness my connection to you gave to me. I wish I could have you back again, but for whatever reason God chose to keep you from me. I have to understand and accept it as I hope you will. Sometimes I feel weak and I complain about the fate that has been dealt to me, but being your mother has taught me to be strong and control my emotions. Being your mother gave me the faith to conquer my fear.

I always wanted my children to respect others and to be respectable themselves, to never be an embarrassment. I also wanted them to be helpful and hopeful. You certainly have lived up to my greatest expectations, for not only have you gained the admiration and the respect of the entire world, but you have helped the world find a new glimmer of hope, hope that some day many more will receive the precious gift of life that was taken from you so prematurely. I am proud of you, and I hope you will be proud of your Daddy and me. He and I both love you very much, and we miss you more than we can ever tell you.

So, my sweetest child of love, I pray that we will someday have the chance to meet again. We must remember to give thanks to God for bringing us together, even though it was only for a short time. I feel greatly honored to have you come into this life of mine, and to see so much of the way things truly are. Please know that you were worth every minute we had together, and if I had it to do all over again, I'd fight for you exactly the same way. I love you baby girl, and I'll always love you forever and forever.

Love,
Mommy

THE END

Order Form

To order additional copies, fill out this form and send it along with your check or money order to: Jarren Press Books, 198 S. Fifth St., Monrovia, CA 91016.

Cost per copy $14.95 plus $1.95 P&H. If shipped to an address in State, include 8% California sales tax.

Ship _____ copies of *Ten Perfect Fingers* to:

Name_____

Address:_____

Address:_____

Address:_____

❑   **Check box for signed copy**
Visit the TPF Web Site at:
http://home.earthlink.net/~mbwinner/tpf.html